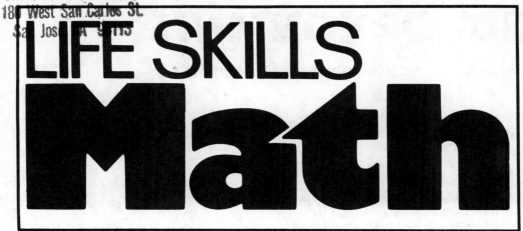

LIFE SKILLS Math

2 EXERCISE SUPPLEMENT

by Donn Mosenfelder

ISBN# 0-87694-159-5   EDI 363

LIFE SKILLS **MATH 2: Exercise Supplement**

TABLE OF CONTENTS

I.   HANDLING MONEY—ADDING AND SUBTRACTING

1. Reading Big Dollar Amounts—Part 1 5-6
2. Reading Big Dollar Amounts—Part 2 6-8
3. Writing Big Dollar Amounts 8-9
4. Comparing Dollar Amounts 10-11
5. Review of Dollar Amounts 12-13
6. Counting Money 14-16
7. Adding Money—Part 1 17-18
8. Adding Money—Part 2 19
9. Adding Bigger Amounts 20-21
10. Subtracting Money 21-22
11. Subtracting Bigger Amounts 23-24
12. Adding Small Change 24-25
13. Making Small Change 26-27
14. Rounding and Estimating 27-28
15. Review of Addition and Subtraction of Dollar Amounts 29-31

II.   HANDLING MONEY—MULTIPLYING AND DIVIDING

16. Multiplying 33-34
17. Multiplying Bigger Amounts 34-35
18. Dividing 36-37
19. Dividing Bigger Amounts 37-38
20. Long Division 39-40
21. Review of Multiplying and Dividing Dollar Amounts 41-42

III. LIFE SKILLS FRACTIONS—ADDING AND SUBTRACTING

22. Life Skills Fractions—Introduction 44-45
23. Reading Fractions 45-46
24. Equal Fractions 46-47
25. Adding Fractions 47-48
26. Subtracting Fractions 48-49
27. Adding and Subtracting Fractions—Part 2 50
28. Adding and Subtracting Fractions with Different Denominators .. 51-52
29. Adding and Subtracting Mixed Fractions 52-53
30. Review of Adding and Subtracting Fractions 54-55

IV.   LIFE SKILLS FRACTIONS—MULTIPLYING AND DIVIDING

31. Multiplying by a Fraction 57
32. Multiplying by a Fraction—Part 2 58
33. Multiplying by a Mixed Fraction 59
34. Fraction Times Fraction 60
35. Dividing Fractions 61
36. Review of Multiplying and Dividing Fractions 62-63

2

V. LIFE SKILLS PERCENTS, DECIMALS, AND HUNDREDTHS

37. Percents, Decimals, and Hundredths—Introduction 65
38. Percents, Decimals, and Hundredths—Part 2 66
39. The Most Common Fractions, Percents, and Decimals 67
40. Adding and Subtracting Percents and Decimals 68-69
41. Multiplying by Decimals—In Life Skills Situations 69-70
42. Multiplying by Percents—In Life Skills Situations 70-71
43. Review of Percents, Decimals, and Hundredths 72-73

VI. LIFE SKILLS WORD PROBLEMS

44. Real World Problems—Add or Subtract? 75
45. Real World Problems—Multiply or Divide? 76
46. Real World Problems—With More than One Step 77-78
47. Real World Problems—Do You Have the Right Information?.... 79-80
48. Price and Cost Comparisons 80-81
49. Price and Cost Comparisons—Part 2 82-83
50. Unit Pricing 84-85
51. Review of Life Skills Word Problems 86-89

VII. STANDARD MEASURES

52. Inches, Feet, and Yards 91
53. Square Inches 92
54. Square Feet and Square Yards 93
55. Ounces and Pounds 94
56. Fluid Ounces, Pints, Quarts, and Gallons 95
57. Metric Measures—Millimeters, Centimeters, and Kilometers 96
58. Metric Measures—Liters and Kilograms 97
59. Review of Standard Measures 98-99

VIII. MISCELLANEOUS LIFE SKILLS MATH

60. Seconds, Minutes, Hours, and Days 101
61. Telling Time 101-102
62. Hours Worked 103
63. A Person's Age 104
64. Graphs 105-106
65. Tables 107-109
66. Freezing, Boiling, and Normal Body Temperature 110
67. Review of Miscellaneous Life Skills Math Problems 111-112

Unit I.
HANDLING MONEY - ADDING AND SUBTRACTING

---

1. Reading Big Dollar Amounts—Part 1

2. Reading Big Dollar Amounts—Part 2

3. Writing Big Dollar Amounts

4. Comparing Dollar Amounts

5. Review of Dollar Amounts

6. Counting Money

7. Adding Money—Part 1

8. Adding Money—Part 2

9. Adding Bigger Amounts

10. Subtracting Money

11. Subtracting Bigger Amounts

12. Adding Small Change

13. Making Small Change

14. Rounding and Estimating

15. Review of Addition and Subtraction of Dollar Amounts

1. Reading Big Dollar Amounts—Part 1

EXERCISES

Write out the dollar amounts in words.

1. $5,000 = _____

2. $15,000 = _____

3. $9,000 = _____

4. $11,000 = _____

5. $85,000 = _____

6. $115,000 = _____

7. $29,000 = _____

8. $50,000 = _____

9. $780,000 = _____

10. $999,000 = _____

11. $1,015,000 = _____

12. $1,780,000 = _____

13. $33,000,000 = _____

_____

_____

14. $48,311,000 = _____

15. $7,705,000 = _____

_____

16. $30,290,000 = _____

_____

_____

17. Last year, Cynthia Smith earned $18,000 = _____

_____

_____

_____

18. John Stepano just bought a new car which cost $9,000 = _____

_____

_____

19. This year's school budget is $4,450,000 = _____

_____

_____

20. Headline in newspaper: **U.S. OFFERS PAKISTAN $400,000,000** = (check one)

☐ four hundred thousand dollars
☐ four hundred million dollars

2. Reading Big Dollar Amounts—Part II

QUICK REMINDER

Watch the number after the comma!

You say the number after the comma like this:
$1,055 = one thousand fifty-five dollars
$3,070,103 = three million, seventy thousand, one hundred three dollars

Watch the number after the decimal!

The number after the decimal tells you how many cents:
$20.76 = twenty dollars and seventy-six cents
$105.00 = one hundred five dollars (Since there are no cents after the decimal point, you don't have to mention them.)
$63,103.04 = sixty-three thousand, one hundred three dollars and four cents

EXERCISES

Write out the dollar amount in words.

1. $4,555.00 = _____

_____

_____

2. $7,023.00 = _____

_____

_____

3. $88,127.00 = _____

_____

_____

4. $5,805.00 = _____

_____

_____

5. $2,125,000.00 = _____

_____

_____

6. $2,125,750.00 = _____

_____

_____

7. $29.40 = _____

_____

_____

8. $29.04 = _____

_____

_____

9. $3,299.04 = _____

_____

_____

10. $7,655.85 = _____

_____

_____

11. $15,420.95 = _____

_____

_____

12. $228,311.12 = _____

_____

_____

13. $4,245,200.50 = _____

_____

_____

14. $2,005,150.90 = _____

_____

_____

15. $726.03 = _____

_____

_____

16. $75,481,055.28 = _____

_____

_____

17. Pat's new washing machine cost $567.45 =

_____

_____

_____

18. The bank gave Melanie a mortgage on her house for $32,405.80 =

_____

_____

_____

19. Match

___ in front of 1 comma   a. cents
___ after the comma   b. dollars (under a thousand)
___ in front of 2 commas   c. thousands
___ after the decimal   d. millions

20. Sandy's airfare to Tokyo was $1,045.00 =

_____

_____

_____

3. Writing Big Dollar Amounts

EXERCISES

Write out all dollar amounts in numbers.

1. six hundred dollars =

$ _____

2. six hundred dollars and twenty cents =

$ _____

3. two thousand, three hundred dollars =

$ _____

4. five thousand, seven hundred and sixty dollars =

$ _____

5. five thousand, seven hundred dollars and sixty cents =

$ _____

6. eight thousand, four hundred fifty-five dollars and seventy-seven cents =

$ _____

7. forty-eight dollars and two cents =

_____

8. ninety-nine dollars and eighty-three cents =

_____

9. four thousand, one hundred and twelve dollars and thirty-three cents =

_____

10. one million, four hundred thousand dollars =

_____

11. one million, four hundred and sixty-six thousand dollars =

_____

12. one million, four hundred and sixty-six thousand dollars and forty-two cents =

_____

13. ninety-one thousand, and thirty-six dollars =

_____

14. one hundred and one dollars and ten cents =

_____

15. seventy-four million, two hundred and eleven thousand, six hundred and five dollars =

_____

16. one hundred twenty-five million, five hundred and seven thousand, nine hundred ninety-nine dollars and twelve cents =

_____

17. A newspaper want-ad says:
    WANTED—SALESPERSON
    EARN TWENTY-FIVE THOUSAND
    PER YEAR

$ _____

18. A lease for an apartment says the yearly rent is thirty-six hundred dollars and eighty-four cents =

$ _____

19. seven hundred and eighteen thousand dollars takes (check one):
    ☐ 1 comma
    ☐ 2 commas

20. three million dollars takes (check one):
    ☐ 1 comma
    ☐ 2 commas

4. Comparing Dollar Amounts

EXERCISES

1. Which amount is smaller? Circle it.
    $583 $573

2. Which amount is larger? Circle it.
    $721 $729

3. Which amount is smaller? Circle it.
    $8,355 $8,381

4. Which amount is smaller? Circle it.
    $2,187,405 $2,129,948

5. Which amount is larger? Circle it.
    $8,808 $8,088

6. Which amount is larger? Circle it.
    $8,808 $8,880

7. Which car is cheaper? Circle it.

$7,488

$7,800

$74,200

8. Which house is cheaper? Circle it.

$71,999

9. Which TV is cheaper? Circle it.

$489 $469

10. Which air fare is cheaper? Circle it.

> **ROUND TRIP TO ATLANTA**
>
> $199

> **ROUND TRIP TO ATLANTA**
>
> $239

11. Put these amounts in order, smallest to largest.
    $4,470 $4,480 $4,450

    $ —————————————— smallest

    $ —————————————— middle

    $ —————————————— largest

12. Put these amounts in order, smallest to largest.
    $5,550 $5,509 $5,590

    $ —————————————— smallest

    $ —————————————— middle

    $ —————————————— largest

13. Put these amounts in order.
    $7,077 $7,700 $7,790

    $ —————————————— smallest

    $ —————————————— middle

    $ —————————————— largest

14. Put these amounts in order.
    $7,077 $7,707 $7,770

    $ —————————————— smallest

    $ —————————————— middle

    $ —————————————— largest

15. Put these amounts in order.
    $9,900 $9,009 $9,100

    $ —————————————— smallest

    $ —————————————— middle

    $ —————————————— largest

16. Put these amounts in order.
    $1,001 $1,100 $1,010

    $ —————————————— smallest

    $ —————————————— middle

    $ —————————————— largest

17. Put these amounts in order.
    $10,600 $10,660 $10,066

    $ —————————————— smallest

    $ —————————————— middle

    $ —————————————— largest

18. Put these amounts in order.
    $29,180 $29,705 $29,199

    $ —————————————— smallest

    $ —————————————— middle

    $ —————————————— largest

19. Put these amounts in order.
    $75,485 $78,333 $78,305

    $ —————————————— smallest

    $ —————————————— middle

    $ —————————————— largest

20. Put these amounts in order.
    $68,909 $69,002 $68,990

    $ —————————————— smallest

    $ —————————————— middle

    $ —————————————— largest

5. Review of Dollar Amounts

EXERCISES

Rewrite each dollar amount. If the amount is in numbers, write it in words. If it is in words, change it to numbers.

1. $49,000 = _____

_____

_____

2. $755,000 = _____

_____

_____

3. $8,205,000 = _____

_____

_____

4. nine hundred ninety-five dollars =

_____

5. two thousand, four hundred and eighteen dollars =

$ _____

6. $604.19 = _____

_____

_____

7. $54,513.00 = _____

_____

_____

8. $7,015.58 = _____

_____

_____

9. $13,388.22 = _____

_____

_____

10. $6,201,888 = _____

_____

_____

11. six hundred twenty-six dollars and seventy-seven cents =

$ _____

12. ninety-nine thousand, eight hundred fifty-six dollars and thirty-nine cents =

$ _____

13. one million, two hundred and eleven thousand, six hundred eighty-four dollars and nine cents =

$ _____

14. The amount of the check is written out here:

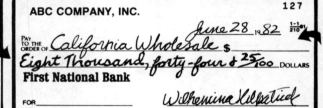

Fill in the same amount in numbers here: _____

15. Which bike is cheaper? Circle it.

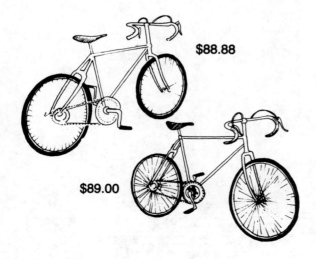

$88.88

$89.00

16. Which amount is larger? Circle it.

$3,338,275 $3,309,948

17. Which amount is smaller? Circle it.

$72,185,000 $72,201,103

18. Put these amounts in order, smallest to largest.

$9,399 $9,939 $9,993

$ ——————————— smallest

$ ——————————— middle

$ ——————————— largest

19. Put these amounts in order.

$17,677 $17,703 $17,710

$ ——————————— smallest

$ ——————————— middle

$ ——————————— largest

20. Put these amounts in order.

$25,305 $25,053 $25,350

$ ——————————— smallest

$ ——————————— middle

$ ——————————— largest

6. Counting Money

EXERCISES

1.

Count how much money is shown above. $ _____

2.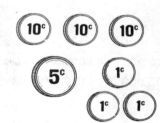

Count how much money is shown above. $ _____

3.

Count how much money is shown above. $ _____

4.

Count how much money is shown above. $ _____

5.

Count how much money is shown above. $ _____

6.

Count how much money is shown above. $ _____

7.

Count how much money is shown above. $ _____

15

8.

Count how much money is shown above. $ ————————————

9.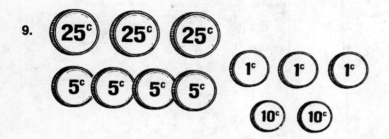

Count how much money is shown above. $ ————————————

10.

Count how much money is shown above. $ ————————————

16

7. Adding Money—Part I

EXERCISES

1. $83.05
    +15.34
    $ _____

2. $743.28
    +145.51
    $ _____

3. $2,004.48
    +5,661.01
    _____

    (Be sure to add the dollar sign
    to the answer.)

4. $95,822.16
    + 3,007.72
    _____

5. $4,323,706.11
    +   16,192.81
    _____

6. $7,185,358.49
    +   604,111.40
    _____

7. Add $23.28 to $65.50

    $ _____

    + _____

8. Add $445.34 to $403.62

    $ _____

    + _____

9. Add $581.27 to $308.12

    $ _____

    + _____

10. Add $22.43 to $956.45

    $ _____

    + _____

11. Add $9.77 to $400.12

    $ _____

    + _____

12. Add $1,328.65 to $7,460.24

    $ _____

    + _____

13. Add $20,139.99 to $75,700.00

    $ _____

    + _____

14. Add $3,242,666.03 to $6,436,200.95

$

+_____

15. Add $585,100.90 to $8,412,722.00

$

+_____

16. Add $7,246.30 to $880,550.50

$

+_____

17. Add $121.40 to $1,384,578.29

$

_____

18. Add these 3 dollar amounts: $32.21 + $24.22 + $12.40

$

_____

19. Add these 3 dollar amounts: $1,005.61 + $5,702.02 + $1,152.15

$

20. Add these 3 dollar amounts: $72,305.00 + $7,223.66 + $441.22

$

8. Adding Money—Part II

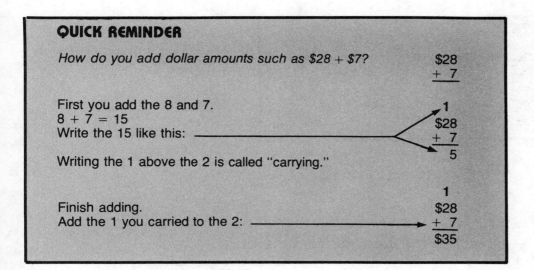

QUICK REMINDER

How do you add dollar amounts such as $28 + $7?

$$\begin{array}{r} \$28 \\ +\ 7 \\ \hline \end{array}$$

First you add the 8 and 7.
8 + 7 = 15
Write the 15 like this:

$$\begin{array}{r} 1 \\ \$28 \\ +\ 7 \\ \hline 5 \end{array}$$

Writing the 1 above the 2 is called "carrying."

Finish adding.
Add the 1 you carried to the 2:

$$\begin{array}{r} 1 \\ \$28 \\ +\ 7 \\ \hline \$35 \end{array}$$

EXERCISES

1. $\begin{array}{r} \$56 \\ +\ 9 \\ \hline \end{array}$

2. $\begin{array}{r} \$83 \\ +\ 8 \\ \hline \end{array}$

3. $\begin{array}{r} \$16 \\ +\ 6 \\ \hline \end{array}$

4. $\begin{array}{r} \$27 \\ +\ 4 \\ \hline \end{array}$

5. $\begin{array}{r} \$12 \\ +\ 8 \\ \hline \end{array}$

6. $\begin{array}{r} \$75 \\ +\ 6 \\ \hline \end{array}$

7. $\begin{array}{r} \$99 \\ +\ 3 \\ \hline \end{array}$

8. $\begin{array}{r} \$34 \\ +\ 6 \\ \hline \end{array}$

9. $\begin{array}{r} \$42 \\ +\ 6 \\ \hline \end{array}$

10. $\begin{array}{r} \$53 \\ +\ 9 \\ \hline \end{array}$

11. $\begin{array}{r} \$71 \\ +\ 9 \\ \hline \end{array}$

12. $\begin{array}{r} \$15 \\ +\ 6 \\ \hline \end{array}$

13. $\begin{array}{r} \$95 \\ +\ 9 \\ \hline \end{array}$

14. $\begin{array}{r} \$88 \\ +\ 8 \\ \hline \end{array}$

15. $\begin{array}{r} \$46 \\ +\ 7 \\ \hline \end{array}$

16. $\begin{array}{r} \$82 \\ +\ 6 \\ \hline \end{array}$

17. $\begin{array}{r} \$24 \\ +\ 7 \\ \hline \end{array}$

18. $\begin{array}{r} \$13 \\ +\ 7 \\ \hline \end{array}$

19. $\begin{array}{r} \$47 \\ +\ 9 \\ \hline \end{array}$

20. $\begin{array}{r} \$91 \\ 9 \\ \hline \end{array}$

9. Adding Bigger Amounts

> **QUICK REMINDER**
>
> *You add bigger amounts the same way you add smaller amounts.*
> Line up commas and decimals. Then start at the far right and add.
> As you go from one column to the next, you sometimes have to
> carry (when the numbers add up to more than 10). Don't forget
> the dollar sign or the decimal point in your answer.

EXERCISES

1. $75.18
　+16.51

2. $23.88
　+20.09

3. $56.68
　+ 2.81

4. $48.14
　+33.39

5. $84.50
　+30.99

6. $703.00
　+ 68.45

7. Add these numbers in a checkbook:

BAL. FOR'D	135	67
DEPOSIT	45	24
TOTAL		

8. $288.88
　+130.31

9. $416.90
　+ 95.06

10. $5,483.18
　+2,707.45

11. $26,095.55
　+ 9,441.62

12. $311,378.61
　+　　435.19

13. $219,008.35
　+145,770.40

14. $7,852,621.35
　+　 47,190.45

15. $25,166,300.00
　+ 3,050,712.30

16. Add $45.25 to $51.90

$

+ _____

17. Add $187.75 to $341.42

$

+ _____

18. Add $27,466.10 to $704.250.75

$

+ _____

19. Add these 3 dollar amounts: $524.77 + $13.18 + $192.05

$

+ _____

20. Add these 3 dollar amounts: $22,651.80 + $3,499.93 + $15,607.62

$

+ _____

10. Subtracting Money

QUICK REMINDER

How do you subtract $45 − $19?

Here's the problem:

$45   You can't subtract
−19   9 from 5.

You have to "borrow" 1 from the 4 in the next column. Here's how you do it:

Borrow 1 from 4   Put the 1 you
− leaves 3 ——→ 3 15   borrowed in
              $4̸5̸ ←   front of the 5
Now subtract. −19
              $26

EXERCISES

1. $80
       −10

2. $80
       −17

3. $46
−17

4. $91
− 5

5. $80
−78

6. $24
−15

7. $32
−15

8. $75
− 6

9. $66
−42

10. $50
−22

11. $15
− 8

12. $74
−69

13. $55
−18

14. $103
− 9

15. $245
− 16

16. $411
−102

17. $290
− 70

18. $608
− 93

19. $274
− 50

20. $977
− 86

11. Subtracting Bigger Amounts

> **QUICK REMINDER**
>
> *You subtract big amounts the same way you subtract smaller amounts.*
> <u>Line up commas</u> and <u>decimals</u>. Then start at the far right and subtract.
> As you go from one column to the next, you sometimes have to <u>borrow</u>.
> Don't forget the <u>dollar sign</u> and the <u>decimal point</u> in your answer.

EXERCISES

1. $904.18
    −353.07

2. $725.20
    −505.18

3. $600.38
    −450.25

4. $837.66
    −145.75

5. $217.77
    − 90.93

6. $4,502.11
    −2,604.03

7. $7,224.48
    −3,116.28

8. $86,383.02
    − 9,252.90

9. $50,368.88
    −41,009.55

10. $111,399.90
    − 25,072.15

11. $565,081.78
    −405,101.50

12. $4,324,528.00
    −2,116,041.10

13. $7,560,731.86
    −1,099,924.38

14. Look at this record of payments you
    are making for a rented car:

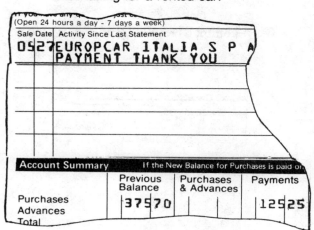

How much is left to pay?

Subtract $125.25 from $375.70

$

−
_____

23

15. Subtract $208.97 from $919.09

$

$-$ _____

16. Subtract $3,266.41 from $8,424.45

$

$-$ _____

17. Subtract $115,000.00 from $702,000.00

$

$-$ _____

18. Subtract $524,890.92 from $611,904.06

$

19. Subtract $788,892.27 from $1,949,207.78

$

20. Subtract $1,405,550.00 from five million dollars

$

12. Adding Small Change

QUICK REMINDER

Small change amounts:

a quarter = 25¢ = $.25
a dime = 10¢ = $.10
a nickel = 5¢ = $.05
a penny = 1¢ = $.01

EXERCISES

Write number amounts out in words. Change word amounts to numbers.

1. $33.38 = thirty-three dollars

and _____ cents

2. $4.05 = four dollars

and _____ cents

3. Three dollars and twenty-four

cents = $ _____

4. Sixteen dollars and seven

cents = $ _____

5. Add 2 quarters + 3 nickels + 3 pennies

$ _____ (2 quarters = $.25 × 2)

_____ (3 nickels = $.05 × 3)

+ _____ (3 pennies = $.03)
$

6. Add 2 dimes + 4 nickels + 4 pennies

$ _____ (2 dimes = $.10 × 2)

_____ (4 nickels = $.05 × 4)

+ _____ (4 pennies = $.04)

7. Add 1 quarter + 3 dimes + 1 nickel

$

_____

8. Add 4 dimes + 7 nickels + 2 pennies

$

_____

9. Add 3 quarters + 8 dimes + 1 nickel + 1 penny

$

_____

10. Add 10 quarters + 12 dimes + 2 nickels

$

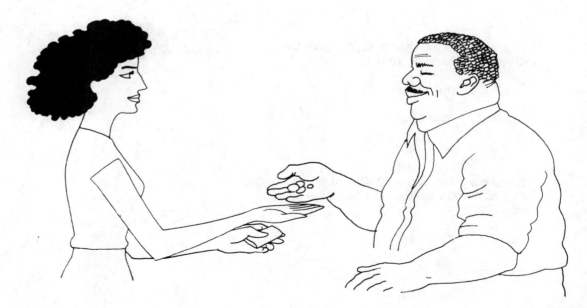

25

13. Making Small Change

EXERCISES

1. A friend owes you $1.45. He gives you $2.00. What coins do you give him in change?

   _____ nickel(s) (to build to $1.50)

   _____ quarter(s) (to get to $2.00)

   (Check your answer:
   Friend gives you: $2.00
   He owes you: − 1.45
   He is owed: $ .55 in change)

2. You owe $3.10 for lunch. You give the cashier $4.00. She gives you:

   _____ nickel(s)

   _____ dime(s)

   _____ quarter(s)

3. You owe $1.73 for shampoo. You give the clerk $2.00. He gives you:

   _____ penny(ies)

   _____ quarter(s)

4. Your sister owes you $.60. She gives you $1.00. What coins do you give her, using the coins below?

   _____ nickel(s)

   _____ dime(s)

   _____ quarter(s)

5. You buy a birthday card for $.82. You give the clerk $1.00. He gives you: (use all the coins below)

   _____ penny(ies)

   _____ nickel(s)

   _____ dime(s)

6. You owe $3.25 to get into the movies. You give the cashier $4.00. She gives you:

7. You owe $1.33 for toothpaste. You give the clerk $2.00. She gives you:

9. You buy $1.15 worth of stamps. You give the Post Office clerk $2.00. She gives you:

8. Your mother owes you $1.29 for the milk you bought. She gives you $1.50. What change do you give her?

10. You owe $9.05 for a shirt. You give the saleslady $10.00. She gives you:

14. Rounding and Estimating

QUICK REMINDER

Sometimes you want to know <u>about how much</u> something will cost.

The best way to find out quickly is to <u>round</u> to the nearest dollar, $10, or $100.

Then you can estimate.

EXERCISES

(Try to figure the questions below in your head.)

1. About how much is $1.99 + $3.99? Round both amounts to nearest dollars. Then add.

Round $1.99 to nearest dollar = $ _____

Round $3.99 to nearest dollar = + _____

The total is <u>about</u> $ _____

2. About how much is $7.95 + $2.95?

$ _____

3. About how much is $12.90 plus $15.00?

$ _____

4. About how much is $10.01 plus $9.98? (<u>Note</u>: this time, you round the $10.01 <u>down</u> to $10.00.)

$_____

5. About how much is $99 plus $199?

$_____

6. About how much is $203 + $395?

$_____

7. About how much is $1,999 + $5,005? (This time, round to the nearest thousand.)

$_____

8. About how much is $29,985 + $12,999?

$_____

9. About how much is $6.99 + $5.99 + $4.99?

$_____

10. About how much is $12,003 + $9,988 + $3,000?

$_____

15. Review of Addition and Subtraction of Dollar Amounts

EXERCISES

1. Count how much money is above. $ ———————————

2. Count how much money is above. $ ———————————

3. $58.50
$+11.49$

$ —————

4. $843.21
$+155.60$

$ —————

5. Add $17.75 to $22.23

$ —————

$+$ —————

6. Add $211.24 to $325.45

$ —————

$+$ —————

7. Add $31,269.40 to $45,020.36

   $

   +_____

8. Add these 3 dollar amounts: $2.41 + $16.03 + $31.41

   $

   +_____

9. $45
   + 9

10. $83
    + 8

11. $76.79
    +19.19

12. $828.09
    + 91.93

13. Add $369.68 to $519.19

    $

    _____

14. Add $42,340.90 to $55,999.03

    $

    _____

15. Add $204,360.60 to $3,477,245.10

    $

    _____

16. $65
    −16

17. $70
    −59

18. $925
    − 72

19. $305.30
    −190.40

20. $24,009.28
    − 6,107.30

21. Subtract $2,821.43 from $6,255.50

    $

    _____

30

22. Subtract $523,456.70 from $1,645,365.81

$ _____

23. Add 4 quarters + 1 dime + 5 nickels + 3 pennies

$ _____

24. Add 6 dimes + 3 nickels + 8 pennies

$ _____

25. A friend owes you $7.20. She gives you $8.00. What coins do you give her in change? (Use all the coins below.)

_____ nickel(s)

_____ quarter(s)

26. You owe $1.08 for a magazine. You give the clerk $1.50. What coins does he give you in change?

27. You owe a friend $3.67. You give her $4.00. What coins does she give you in change?

28. About how much is $15.95 + $7.95? (Round and estimate. Try to figure it out in your head.)

$ _____

29. About how much is $11,980 + $14,010? (Round and estimate. Try to figure it out in your head.)

$ _____

30. About how much is $2,999 + $5,000 + $4,980? (Round and estimate. Try to figure it out in your head.)

$ _____

Unit II.
HANDLING MONEY - MULTIPLYING AND DIVIDING

16. Multiplying

17. Multiplying Bigger Amounts

18. Dividing

19. Dividing Bigger Amounts

20. Long Division

21. Review of Multiplying and Dividing Dollar Amounts

16. Multiplying

EXERCISES

1. $28
   × 3

2. $44
   × 4

3. $28
   × 6

4. $51
   × 7

5. $93
   × 5

6. $80
   × 9

7. $18
   × 6

8. $42
   × 7

9. $86
   × 2

10. $95
    × 5

11. $25
    × 2

12. $76
    × 4

13. $46
    × 9

14. You need 7 pieces of plywood for a room you are building. They cost $18 each. How much for all 7?

    $18
    × 7 pieces of plywood

15. You want to buy 4 kitchen chairs. They cost $36 each. How much for all 4?

$36
× 4

16. How much is $77 × 6?

$

17. How much is $29 × 8?

17. Multiplying Bigger Amounts

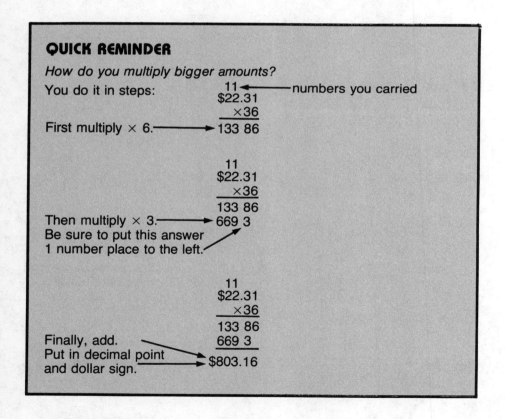

QUICK REMINDER

How do you multiply bigger amounts?

You do it in steps:

First multiply × 6.

Then multiply × 3.
Be sure to put this answer
1 number place to the left.

Finally, add.
Put in decimal point
and dollar sign.

11 ← numbers you carried
$22.31
×36
133 86

11
$22.31
×36
133 86
669 3

11
$22.31
×36
133 86
669 3
$803.16

EXERCISES

1. $16.25
× 21

2. $42.03
× 55

3. $18.88
× 19

4. $52.34
× 26

5. $80.09
× 38

6. $72.70
× 84

7. $92.56
× 42

8. $28.17
× 64

9. $33.09
× 53

10. $89.99
× 32

11. $82.46
× 48

12. $75.62
× 25

13. $34.50
× 29

14. $73.85
× 13

15. $60.56
× 57

16. $73.51
× 18

17. The ABC Corp. wants to buy 12 file cabinets. They cost $65.85 each. How much for all 12?

$65.85
× 12

18. How much is $92.15 × 59?

$

19. How much is $14.63 × 70?

20. How much is $90.21 × 15?

18. Dividing

EXERCISES

1. $3\overline{)\$28}$ 6. $5\overline{)\$59}$ 11. $4\overline{)\$47}$

2. $6\overline{)\$51}$ 7. $4\overline{)\$90}$ 12. $3\overline{)\$38}$

3. $5\overline{)\$17}$ 8. $7\overline{)\$38}$ 13. $6\overline{)\$45}$

4. $7\overline{)\$60}$ 9. $9\overline{)\$81}$ 14. $5\overline{)\$91}$

5. $2\overline{)\$86}$ 10. $9\overline{)\$86}$ 15. $7\overline{)\$18}$

16. Divide $22 by 5

17. Divide $73 by 8

18. Divide $40 by 7

19. Six yards of material cost you $45. How much did each yard cost?

6)$45

20. A set of 8 cups and saucers cost $29. How much did each cup and saucer cost?

8)$29

19. Dividing Bigger Amounts

QUICK REMINDER

How do you divide bigger amounts such as 4)$9.53?

Step 1. You already know how to divide 9 by 4.

```
        $2.
    4 )$9.53
      −8
       1
```

Step 2. Bring down the next number, the 5. Now you have 15. Divide it by 4. Multiply and subtract again.

```
           $2.3 ←——— 15 divided by 4
       4 )$9.53
         −8 ↓
          1 5
          1 2 ←——You multiply 3 × 4.
Subtract 3 from 12.——→ 3
```

Step 3. Bring down the next number, the 2. Divide again by 4. Multiply. Subtract.

```
        $2.38
    4 )$9.53
      −8 |
       1 5|
      −1 2↓
         33
        −32
          1
```

The answer is $2.38 R1 or 2.38\frac{1}{4}$, which means $\frac{1}{4}$ cent is left over.

EXERCISES

1. 3)$16.50

2. 6)$29.99

3. 5)$20.02

4. 9) $90.36

5. 6) $2.85

6. 2) $48.37

7. 4) $20.20

8. 8) $35.87

9. 7) $5.25

10. 8) $16.17

11. 3) $40.00

12. 5) $78.93

13. 4) $180.20

14. 2) $627.30

15. 5) $201.37

16. 9) $275.30

17. How much is $515.89 divided by 2?

2) $515.89

18. How much is $47.77 divided by 8?

8) $47.77

19. How much is $324.56 divided by 6?

)

20. You and 2 friends share an apartment. The monthly rent is $469.20. How much per month does it cost each of you?

3) $469.20

20. Long Division

QUICK REMINDER

How do you divide even bigger amounts such as 12) $4,140.36 ?

Put dollar sign and decimal up top—directly above.

Then divide the 12 into the first number bigger
than 12. (4 is too small, so divide into 41.)

```
                                    $  3    .
                                 12 ) $4,140.36
```

- 12 into 41 = 3
- Multiply 3 × 12 = 36
- Subtract 41 − 36 = 5 left over,
  and bring down the 4 = 54

```
                        −  36 ↓
                           54
```

Keep going. 12 into 54 = 4.
4 × 12 = 48. Subtract. Bring down the 0.
12 into 60 = 5.   5 × 12 = 60.
Subtract. No remainder. Bring down the 3.
12 doesn't go into 3. Write down 0 above.
Then bring down the 6 and keep going.
12 into 36 = 3.   3 × 12 = 36, no remainder.

```
          $  345.03
       12 ) $4,140.36
         −  36 ↓
            54
          − 48 ↓
            60
          − 60 ↓
            036
           − 36
             0
```

NOTE: If you are not sure how many times
one number divides into another, guess.
- Then multiply and subtract.
- If you were wrong, try again.

EXERCISES

1. 23) $48.50

2. 11) $67.21

3. 30) $16.05

4. 35) $77.77

5. 42) $65.80

6. 51) $120.18

7. 13)$275.60

12. 37)$282.66

17. Divide 43 into $720.03

43)$720.03

8. 62)$72.00

13. 64)$285.21

18. Divide 25 into $155.60

)

9. 29)$352.11

14. 91)$100.00

19. Divide 68 into $103.45

10. 44)$525.89

15. 18)$67.27

20. Divide 82 into $975.64

11. 72)$326.80

16. Divide 56 into $189.89

56)$189.89

21. Review of Multiplying and Dividing Dollar Amounts

EXERCISES

1. $39
   × 7

2. $75
   × 4

3. $49
   × 9

4. $87
   × 3

5. $12.88
   ×   2

6. $90.40
   ×   9

7. $20.13
   ×   5

8. $38.44
   ×   7

9. $67.89
   ×   5

10. $19.09
    ×   6

11. 5) $53

12. 9) $84

13. 3) $155

14. 6) $298

15. 3) $7.04

16. 8) $25.46

17. 5) $52.63

18. 3) $482.75

21. 14) $89.25

24. Divide 74 into $921.50

19. 8) $711.09

22. 63) $105.22

25. Divide 88 into $7,025.64

20. 7) $4,366.65

23. 54) $249.73

Unit III.
LIFE SKILLS FRACTIONS - ADDING AND SUBTRACTING

---

22. Life Skills Fractions—Introduction
23. Reading Fractions
24. Equal Fractions
25. Adding Fractions
26. Subtracting Fractions
27. Adding and Subtracting Fractions—Part 2
28. Adding and Subtracting Fractions with Different Denominators
29. Adding and Subtracting Mixed Fractions
30. Review of Adding and Subtracting Fractions

22. Life Skills Fractions—Introduction

QUICK REMINDER

This cup is divided into 3 equal parts, or thirds. Each part is called $\frac{1}{3}$.

This pound of butter is divided into 4 equal parts, or quarters. Each part is called $\frac{1}{4}$.

EXERCISES

For the following questions, fill in the missing number in the fraction.

1. Some measuring cups are divided into 4 equal parts.

Each part is called $\dfrac{1}{\boxed{}}$

(Fill in the number.)

2. Other measuring cups are divided into 6 equal parts.

Each part is called $\dfrac{1}{\boxed{}}$

(Fill in the number.)

5. On this ruler, each inch is divided into 16 equal parts.

Each part is called $\dfrac{1}{\boxed{}}$ inch.

3. A foot has 12 inches.

Each inch $= \dfrac{1}{\boxed{}}$ foot

6. There are 24 hours in a day.

Each hour $= \dfrac{1}{\boxed{}}$ day.

4. A yard has 3 feet.

Each foot $= \dfrac{1}{\boxed{}}$ yard

7. There are 60 minutes in an hour.

Each minute $= \dfrac{\boxed{}}{\boxed{}}$ hour.

(Fill in top <u>and</u> bottom.)

8. There are 9 square feet in 1 square yard.

Each square foot = $\dfrac{\square}{\square}$ square yard.

10. There are 8 fluid ounces in 1 cup.

Each fluid ounce = $\dfrac{\square}{\square}$ cup.

9. There are 2 cups in 1 pint.

Each cup = $\dfrac{\square}{\square}$ pint.

23. Reading Fractions

QUICK REMINDER

$\dfrac{1}{2}$ = one **half**

$\dfrac{1}{3}$ = one **third**

$\dfrac{1}{6}$ = one **sixth**

$\dfrac{1}{10}$ = one **tenth**

$\dfrac{1}{25}$ = one **twenty-fifth**

$\dfrac{1}{50}$ = one **fiftieth**

$\dfrac{1}{100}$ = one **one-hundredth**

$\dfrac{2}{3}$ = **two** thirds

$\dfrac{5}{6}$ = **five** sixths

$\dfrac{7}{10}$ = **seven** tenths

$\dfrac{2}{25}$ = **two** twenty-fifths

$\dfrac{49}{50}$ = **forty-nine** fiftieths

$\dfrac{99}{100}$ = **ninety-nine** one-hundredths

EXERCISES

1. One eighth of an inch = $\dfrac{\square}{\square}$ inch.

2. $\dfrac{7}{8}$ inch = —————— inch.

3. One half of a mile = $\dfrac{\square}{\square}$ mile.

4. $\dfrac{3}{4}$ mile = —————— mile.

5. You need $\dfrac{7}{10}$ yards of materials = —————— yards.

6. One tenth of the budget = $\dfrac{\square}{\square}$ budget.

7. Five-sixths of a cup = $\dfrac{\boxed{}}{\boxed{}}$ cup.

9. $\dfrac{5}{100}$ = _____ cup.

8. $\dfrac{1}{3}$ cup = _____ cup.

10. Seventy-five one-hundredths = $\dfrac{\boxed{}}{\boxed{}}$

24. Equal Fractions

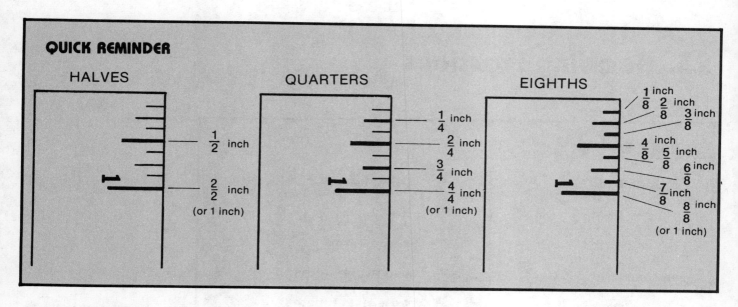

QUICK REMINDER

HALVES

$\dfrac{1}{2}$ inch

$\dfrac{2}{2}$ inch
(or 1 inch)

QUARTERS

$\dfrac{1}{4}$ inch

$\dfrac{2}{4}$ inch

$\dfrac{3}{4}$ inch

$\dfrac{4}{4}$ inch
(or 1 inch)

EIGHTHS

$\dfrac{1}{8}$ inch

$\dfrac{2}{8}$ inch

$\dfrac{3}{8}$ inch

$\dfrac{4}{8}$ inch

$\dfrac{5}{8}$ inch

$\dfrac{6}{8}$ inch

$\dfrac{7}{8}$ inch

$\dfrac{8}{8}$ inch
(or 1 inch)

EXERCISES

Fill in the missing number of the fractions below. To figure out these exercises, refer to the illustration above.

1. $1 = \dfrac{\boxed{}}{4}$

2. $1 = \dfrac{\boxed{}}{8}$

3. $\dfrac{1}{4} = \dfrac{\boxed{}}{8}$

4. $\dfrac{1}{2} = \dfrac{\boxed{}}{8}$

5. $\dfrac{3}{4} = \dfrac{\boxed{}}{8}$

6. $\dfrac{4}{4} = \dfrac{\boxed{}}{8}$

7. Which is bigger? Circle your answer.

$\dfrac{1}{4}$ $\dfrac{5}{8}$

8. Which is bigger?

$\dfrac{1}{2}$ $\dfrac{3}{8}$

9. Which is bigger?

$$\frac{1}{2} \qquad \frac{3}{4}$$

10. Which is bigger?

$$\frac{5}{8} \qquad \frac{7}{8}$$

11. Which is bigger?

$$\frac{3}{4} \qquad \frac{7}{8}$$

12. $\frac{1}{2} = \frac{2}{4} = \dfrac{\boxed{}}{6}$

(You won't find the answer in the illustrations. But you should be able to figure it out.)

13. $\frac{1}{2} = \frac{2}{4} = \dfrac{\boxed{}}{8}$

14. Which of these fractions $= \frac{1}{2}$?

(You won't find the answer to this one in the illustrations, either. But you should be able to figure it out.)

$$\frac{1}{10} \qquad \frac{5}{10} \qquad \frac{3}{10} \qquad \frac{7}{10}$$

15. Which of these fractions $= \frac{1}{4}$?

$$\frac{4}{16} \qquad \frac{5}{16} \qquad \frac{9}{16} \qquad \frac{12}{16}$$

16. Which of these is bigger?

$$\frac{7}{11} \qquad \frac{9}{11}$$

17. Which of these is bigger?

$$\frac{1}{2} \qquad \frac{3}{5}$$

18. Which of these is bigger?

$$\frac{1}{4} \qquad \frac{1}{8}$$

19. Which of these is bigger?

$$\frac{1}{4} \qquad \frac{1}{5}$$

20. Which of these fractions $= \frac{1}{8}$?

$$\frac{1}{16} \qquad \frac{2}{16} \qquad \frac{3}{16} \qquad \frac{4}{16}$$

25. Adding Fractions

QUICK REMINDER

How do you add such Life Skills fractions as $\frac{3}{4}$ inch $+ \frac{1}{4}$ inch?

It's easy. They both have the same denominators (bottom part). So you simply add the numerators (top part)!

$\frac{3}{4}$ inch $+ \frac{1}{4}$ inch $= \frac{4}{4}$ inch.

But as you know, $\frac{4}{4} = 1$. (This is called "writing your answer in the simplest form.") So $\frac{3}{4}$ inch $+ \frac{1}{4}$ inch $= \frac{4}{4}$ inch $= 1$ inch.

EXERCISES

Fill in the missing numbers.

1. $\frac{1}{3}$ cup $+ \frac{1}{3}$ cup $= \dfrac{\boxed{}}{\boxed{}}$ cup

(Write your answer in the simplest form.)

2. $\frac{1}{3}$ cup $+ \frac{2}{3}$ cup $= \dfrac{\boxed{}}{\boxed{}}$ cup $=$ ———— cup

47

3. $\frac{1}{5}$ yard $+\frac{1}{5}$ yard $=\frac{\square}{\square}$ yard

4. $\frac{1}{5}$ yard $+\frac{1}{5}$ yard $+\frac{1}{5}$ yard $=\frac{\square}{\square}$ yard

5. $\frac{1}{8}$ inch $+\frac{7}{8}$ inch $=\frac{\square}{\square}$ inch $=$ ———— inch

6. $\frac{3}{10}$ mile $+\frac{6}{10}$ mile $=\frac{\square}{\square}$ mile

7. $\frac{3}{8}$ pound $+\frac{5}{8}$ pound $=$ ————

(If you can write your answer in a simpler form, do so.)

8. $\frac{99}{100} + \frac{1}{100} =$ ————

(if you can write your answer in a simpler form, do so.)

9. $\frac{3}{16} + \frac{12}{16} =$ ————

(If you can write your answer in a simpler form, do so.)

10. $\frac{3}{16} + \frac{12}{16} + \frac{1}{16} =$ ————

(If you can write your answer in a simpler form, do so.)

26. Subtracting Fractions

QUICK REMINDER

How do you subtract such Life Skills fractions as $\frac{3}{4}$ mile $-\frac{1}{4}$ mile?
It's easy. The denominators (bottom part) are the same. So you can simply subtract the numerators.

$\frac{3}{4}$ mi. $-\frac{1}{4}$ mi. $=\frac{2}{4}$ mi.

But as you know, $\frac{2}{4} = \frac{1}{2}$. (This is also called "simplifying", or writing

your answer in the simplest form.) So $\frac{3}{4}$ mi. $-\frac{1}{4}$ mi. $=\frac{2}{4}$ mi. $=\frac{1}{2}$ mi.

EXERCISES

Fill in the missing numbers.

1. $\frac{4}{5}$ yard $-\frac{1}{5}$ yard $=\frac{\square}{\square}$ yard

(Write your answer in the simplest form.)

2. $\frac{5}{8}$ yd. $-\frac{1}{8}$ yd. $=\frac{\square}{\square}$ yd. $=\frac{\square}{\square}$ yd.

3. $\dfrac{9}{16}$ mi. $-\dfrac{1}{16}$ mi. $=\dfrac{\square}{\square}$ mi. $=\dfrac{\square}{\square}$ mi.

(Write your answer in the simplest form.)

4. $\dfrac{2}{3}$ cup $-\dfrac{1}{3}$ cup $=\dfrac{\square}{\square}$ cup

5. $\dfrac{5}{8}$ in. $-\dfrac{1}{8}$ in. $=\dfrac{\square}{\square}$ in. $=\dfrac{\square}{\square}$ in.

6. $\dfrac{3}{8}$ inch $-\dfrac{2}{8}$ inch $=\dfrac{\square}{\square}$ inch

7. $\dfrac{6}{10}$ meter $-\dfrac{5}{10}$ meter $=\dfrac{\square}{\square}$ meter

8. $\dfrac{8}{10}$ liter $-\dfrac{1}{10}$ liter $=\dfrac{\square}{\square}$ liter

9. $\dfrac{8}{10}$ pound $-\dfrac{3}{10}$ pound $=$ _____

(If you can write your answer in a simpler form, do so.)

10. $\dfrac{11}{12}$ year $-\dfrac{5}{12}$ year $=$ _____

(If you can write your answer in a simpler form, do so.)

27. Adding and Subtracting Fractions—Part II

QUICK REMINDER

How do you subtract such Life Skills fractions as $\frac{7}{8}$ yd. $-\frac{1}{8}$ yd.?

$\frac{7}{8}$ yd. $-\frac{1}{8}$ yd. $=\frac{6}{8}$ yd. (Denominators are the same. You can subtract the numerators.)

But you can simplify $\frac{6}{8}$. Divide both the top and the bottom by 2.

$$\frac{6\div2}{8\div2} = \frac{3}{4}$$

Here's a quick way to write the same thing $\quad \frac{\overset{3}{\cancel{6}}}{\underset{4}{\cancel{8}}} = \frac{3}{4}$

So $\frac{7}{8}$ yd. $-\frac{1}{8}$ yd. $= \frac{\overset{3}{\cancel{6}}}{\underset{4}{\cancel{8}}}$ yd. $= \frac{3}{4}$ yd.

What do you do when your answer comes out to a fraction such as $\frac{16}{10}$?

$\frac{16}{10}$ is the same as $1\frac{6}{10}$, since $\frac{10}{10} = 1$ and then there are $\frac{6}{10}$ left over. But $1\frac{6}{10}$ can also be simplified. Divide top and bottom of the fraction by 2:

$$1\frac{\overset{3}{\cancel{6}}}{\underset{5}{\cancel{10}}} = 1\frac{3}{5}. \text{ So: } \frac{16}{10} = 1\frac{\overset{3}{\cancel{6}}}{\underset{5}{\cancel{10}}} = 1\frac{3}{5}.$$

EXERCISES

(Always write your answers in the simplest form.)

1. $\frac{5}{8}$ mi. $+\frac{1}{8}$ mi. = —————— mi. = —————— mi.

2. $\frac{9}{10}$ meter $-\frac{3}{10}$ meter = —————— meter = —————— meter

3. $\frac{3}{5}$ mi. $+\frac{4}{5}$ mi. = —————— mi. = —————— mi.

4. $\frac{7}{16}$ in. $-\frac{3}{16}$ in. = —————— in.

5. $\frac{1}{3}$ cup $+\frac{1}{3}$ cup = —————— cup

6. $\frac{4}{10}$ liter $-\frac{1}{10}$ liter = —————— liter

7. $\frac{7}{8}$ lb. $-\frac{1}{8}$ lb. = —————— lb.

8. $\frac{9}{16}$ in. $+\frac{9}{16}$ in. = —————— in.

9. $\frac{7}{10}$ second $+\frac{9}{10}$ second = —————— second

10. $\frac{5}{6}$ cup $-\frac{1}{6}$ cup = —————— cup

28. Adding and Subtracting Fractions with Different Denominators

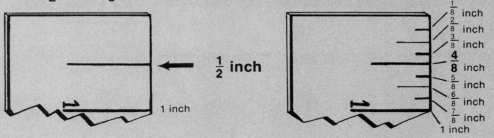
EXERCISES

1. Subtract: $\frac{1}{2}$ mi. − $\frac{1}{4}$ mi.
(To figure out this problem, change

$\frac{1}{2}$ to $\frac{\square}{4}$. Then you can subtract.)

$\frac{1}{2}$ mi. − $\frac{1}{4}$ mi. = $\frac{\square}{4}$ mi. −

$\frac{1}{4}$ mi. = _____ mi.

2. Add $\frac{3}{10}$ mi. + $\frac{1}{5}$ mi.
(This time, change $\frac{1}{5}$ to $\frac{\square}{10}$.
Then you can add.)

$\frac{3}{10}$ mi. + $\frac{1}{5}$ mi. = $\frac{3}{10}$ min. +

$\frac{\square}{10}$ mi. = _____ mi.

3. $\frac{1}{8}$ in. + $\frac{1}{4}$ in. = $\frac{1}{8}$ in. + $\frac{\square}{\square}$ in. = _____ in.

4. $\frac{3}{16}$ in. − $\frac{1}{8}$ in. = $\frac{3}{16}$ in. − $\frac{\square}{\square}$ in. = _____ in.

5. $\frac{5}{6}$ cup − $\frac{1}{3}$ cup = $\frac{5}{6}$ cup − $\frac{\square}{\square}$ = _____ cup =

_____ cup (Write your answer in its simplest form.)

6. $\frac{3}{4}$ yd. − $\frac{1}{8}$ yd. = _____
(Simplify your answer if you can.)

7. $\frac{9}{10}$ mi. + $\frac{1}{5}$ mi. = _____
(Simplify your answer if you can.)

8. $\frac{3}{8}$ lb. $+ \frac{1}{2}$ lb. = _____
(Simplify your answer if you can.)

10. $\frac{1}{6}$ cup $+ \frac{5}{6}$ cup $+ \frac{1}{3}$ cup = _____
(Simplify your answer if you can.)

9. $\frac{1}{8}$ lb. $+ \frac{3}{8}$ lb. $+ \frac{1}{2}$ lb. = _____
(Simplify your answer if you can.)

29. Adding and Subtracting Mixed Fractions

QUICK REMINDER

How do you add such Life Skills fractions as $2\frac{3}{4}$ yd. $+ 3\frac{1}{4}$ yd.?

Number like $2\frac{3}{4}$ and $3\frac{1}{4}$ are called mixed fractions. This means they contain both a whole number and a fraction. To add mixed numbers, first add the fractions. Then add the whole numbers:

$$\begin{array}{r} 2\frac{3}{4} \\ + 3\frac{1}{4} \\ \hline 5\frac{4}{4} \end{array}$$

Now simplify. $5\frac{4}{4} = 6$ since $\frac{4}{4} = 1$

So: $2\frac{3}{4}$ yd. $+ 3\frac{1}{4}$ yd. $= 5\frac{4}{4}$ yd. $= 6$ yd.

Here's another problem: $5\frac{1}{8}$ feet $+ 4\frac{1}{4}$ feet. As you might guess, you can't add $5\frac{1}{8} + 4\frac{1}{4}$ until you make the denominators of both fractions the same: $4\frac{1}{4} = 4\frac{2}{8}$

So: $\quad 5\frac{1}{8}$ ft. $+ 4\frac{1}{4}$ ft. $= \begin{array}{r} 5\frac{1}{8} \text{ ft.} \\ + 4\frac{2}{8} \text{ ft.} \\ \hline 9\frac{3}{8} \text{ ft.} \end{array}$

EXERCISES   To answer each question below, first change any fractions you have to. Remember to simplify answers if you can.

1. Subtract: $3\frac{2}{3}$ cup $- 1\frac{1}{3}$ cup

$$\begin{array}{r} \\ - \underline{} \\ \hline \end{array}$$

2. Add: $5\frac{7}{8}$ in. $+ 3\frac{1}{4}$ in.

$$\begin{array}{r} \\ + \underline{} \\ \hline \end{array}$$

3. Subtract: $4\frac{3}{10}$ meter $- 3\frac{1}{10}$ meter

4. Add: $2\frac{7}{10}$ mi. $+ 1\frac{1}{5}$ mi.

5. $9\frac{1}{4}$ yd. $+ 1\frac{3}{4}$ yd.

6. $2\frac{1}{2}$ lb. $+ 1\frac{5}{8}$ lb.

7. Add these 3 lengths together:

$3\frac{1}{8}$ in. $+ 1\frac{1}{8}$ in. $+ 5\frac{1}{2}$ in.

8. Add these 3 lengths together:

$1\frac{1}{4}$ in. $+ 3\frac{3}{4}$ in. $+ 1\frac{1}{2}$ in.

9. Add these 3 weights together:

$1\frac{1}{10}$ lb. $+ 4\frac{1}{2}$ lb. $+ 1\frac{1}{5}$ lb.

(To do this problem, change all the fractions to tenths.)

10. Add these 4 distances together:

$1\frac{3}{8}$ mi. $+ 1\frac{1}{4}$ mi. $+ 1\frac{1}{8}$ mi. $+ 1\frac{1}{2}$ mi.

53

30. Review of Adding and Subtracting Fractions

EXERCISES

1. On the ruler, each inch is divided into 8 equal parts. Each part is called $\frac{\square}{\square}$

2. There are 100 centimeters in 1 meter. Each centimeter = $\frac{\square}{\square}$ meter.

3. There are 16 ounces in a pound. Each ounce = $\frac{\square}{\square}$ pound.

4. One quarter of an inch = $\frac{\square}{\square}$ in.

5. $\frac{9}{10}$ km = _____ km

6. Ninety-nine one-hundredths = $\frac{\square}{\square}$

7. $\frac{1}{4} = \frac{\square}{8}$

8. $\frac{1}{3} = \frac{\square}{6}$

9. $\frac{1}{2} = \frac{\square}{8}$

10. $\frac{1}{2} = \frac{\square}{10}$

11. $\frac{3}{4} = \frac{\square}{8}$

12. $\frac{7}{8} = \frac{\square}{16}$

13. Which is bigger? (Circle your answer.)

$\frac{3}{8}$ $\qquad$ $\frac{1}{4}$

14. Which is bigger?

$\frac{1}{2}$ $\qquad$ $\frac{2}{3}$

15. Which is bigger?

$\frac{7}{8}$ $\qquad$ $\frac{3}{4}$

16. Which of these fractions = $\frac{1}{2}$?

$\frac{8}{16}$ $\qquad$ $\frac{9}{16}$ $\qquad$ $\frac{10}{16}$ $\qquad$ $\frac{12}{16}$

17. $\frac{1}{6}$ cup + $\frac{1}{6}$ cup = _____
(Simplify your answers whenever you can.)

18. $\frac{3}{16}$ in. + $\frac{7}{16}$ in. = _____

19. $\frac{1}{8}$ mi. + $\frac{7}{8}$ mi. = _____

20. $\frac{1}{8}$ yd. + $\frac{3}{8}$ yd. + $\frac{5}{8}$ yd. = _____

21. $\frac{3}{8}$ in. − $\frac{1}{8}$ in. = _____

22. $\frac{7}{10}$ meter − $\frac{1}{10}$ meter = _____

23. $\frac{3}{5}$ min. − $\frac{1}{5}$ min. = _____

24. $\frac{1}{4}$ in. + $\frac{1}{8}$ in. = _____
(Make denominators of fractions the same whenever you have to.)

25. $\frac{1}{4}$ in. $- \frac{1}{8}$ in. = _____

(Make denominators the same whenever you have to and simplify your answers whenever you can.)

26. $\frac{1}{2}$ mi. $- \frac{3}{16}$ mi. = _____

27. $\frac{7}{10}$ lb. $+ \frac{3}{5}$ lb. = _____

28. $\frac{1}{2}$ ounce $+ \frac{1}{16}$ ounce = _____

29. $\frac{5}{8}$ yd. $+ \frac{1}{8}$ yd. $+ \frac{3}{4}$ yd. = _____

30. $\frac{7}{16}$ in. $+ \frac{1}{8}$ in. $+ \frac{3}{16}$ in. = _____

31. $5\frac{7}{8}$ yd. $+ 4\frac{1}{8}$ yd. = _____

32. $6\frac{1}{2}$ ft. $- 3\frac{1}{6}$ ft. = _____

33. $2\frac{1}{2}$ lb. $- 1\frac{1}{4}$ lb. = _____

34. Add these 3 lengths together:

$\frac{7}{8}$ in. $+ 1\frac{1}{8}$ in. $+ 1\frac{3}{4}$ in.

35. Add these 4 distances together:

$3\frac{1}{4}$ mi. $+ 5\frac{1}{2}$ mi. $+ 2\frac{1}{8}$ mi. $+ 1\frac{7}{8}$ mi.

Unit IV.
LIFE SKILLS FRACTIONS - MULTIPLYING AND DIVIDING

31. Multiplying by a Fraction

32. Multiplying by a Fraction—Part 2

33. Multiplying by a Mixed Fraction

34. Fraction Times Fraction

35. Dividing Fractions

36. Review of Multiplying and Dividing Fractions

31. Multiplying by a Fraction

EXERCISES

1. $3 \times \frac{1}{8}$ inch = _____

2. $2 \times \frac{3}{10}$ meter = _____
   (Simplify answers whenever you can.)

3. $7 \times \frac{1}{6}$ cup = _____
   (Continue to simplify answers whenever you can.)

4. $2 \times \frac{3}{4}$ hours = _____

5. $3 \times \frac{5}{8}$ in. = _____

6. $8 \times \frac{1}{10}$ second = _____

7. You have to walk $\frac{3}{4}$ mile to work 5 days a week. How many miles per week is this?

   $5 \times \frac{3}{4}$ mile = _____

8. You plan to glue 2 boards together. Each board is $\frac{7}{8}$ in. thick. How thick are the 2 boards together?

   $2 \times \frac{7}{8}$ in. = _____

9. You are planning a meal. You will need $\frac{1}{2}$ lb. of meat for each person. There are 12 of you. How many pounds of meat will you need altogether?

   $12 \times \frac{1}{2}$ lb. = _____

10. Each house in your community has $\frac{1}{4}$ acre of land. There are 24 houses. How many acres of land are there altogether?

    _____

32. Multiplying by a fraction—Part II

EXERCISES

1. $\frac{1}{2} \times \$4.50 =$ _____

2. $\frac{1}{4} \times \$ .96 =$ _____

3. $\frac{2}{5} \times \$3.95 =$ _____

4. $\frac{1}{6} \times 1{,}100$ miles $=$ _____

5. $\frac{3}{8}$ in. $\times 64 =$ _____

6. $\frac{3}{4} \times \$240 =$ _____

7. $\frac{7}{10} \times 70$ years $=$ _____

8. Asparagus costs \$1.89 per pound. You have picked $\frac{2}{3}$ pound. How much does it cost?

   $\frac{2}{3} \times \$1.89 =$ _____

9. Tomatoes cost \$.99 per pound. You have picked out $\frac{2}{3}$ pound. How much do the tomatoes cost?

   _____

10. Hamburger costs \$2.20 per pound. You need $\frac{3}{4}$ pound. How much will the hamburger cost?

    _____

33. Multiplying by a Mixed Fraction

QUICK REMINDER

How do you multiply in such Life Skills problems as $1\frac{1}{2} \times \$6$?

First change $1\frac{1}{2}$ (a mixed fraction) to a regular fraction:

Since $1 = \frac{2}{2}$, $1\frac{1}{2} = \frac{2}{2} + \frac{1}{2} = \frac{3}{2}$.

So: $1\frac{1}{2} \times \$6 = \frac{3}{2} \times \$6$.

Simplify: $\frac{3}{2} \times \$6 = \frac{3 \times \$3}{1} = \$9$

EXERCISES

1. $3\frac{1}{2} \times \$20$ = _____

   (First change $3\frac{1}{2}$ to a regular fraction.)

2. $1\frac{1}{6} \times \$1.20$ = _____

3. $4\frac{1}{4} \times \$100$ = _____

4. $2\frac{1}{8} \times 16$ ounces = _____

5. $3\frac{3}{5} \times \$2.50$ = _____

6. $1\frac{7}{8} \times 480$ miles = _____

7. $5\frac{1}{2} \times 300$ lbs. = _____

8. Tomatoes cost $.69 per pound. You have picked out $2\frac{1}{3}$ lbs. How much will they cost?

   $2\frac{1}{3} \times \$.69$ = _____

9. You are planning a trip. You figure you will drive about 400 miles per day. About how far will you drive in $2\frac{1}{2}$ days?

   $2\frac{1}{2} \times 400$ mi. = _____

10. At 400 mi. per day, how far will you travel in $3\frac{3}{4}$ days?

   _____

34. Fraction Times Fraction

EXERCISES

1. $\frac{1}{4} \times \frac{3}{5}$ lb. = _____

2. $\frac{1}{3} \times \frac{3}{10}$ meter = _____

3. $\frac{4}{5} \times \frac{7}{10}$ mi. = _____

4. $\frac{9}{10} \times \frac{1}{4}$ ounce = _____

5. $\frac{2}{3}$ yd. $\frac{3}{4}$ yd. = _____

6. $\frac{1}{2} \times \frac{1}{6}$ cup = _____

7. $\frac{2}{7} \times \frac{2}{3}$ acre = _____

8. You have $\frac{3}{4}$ acre of land. You want to divide it into 6 equal plots for tent sites. Each tent site will be $\frac{1}{6}$ of the land, or:

_____

9. You have $\frac{9}{10}$ lb. of powder. You want to put equal amounts in 9 cups. The powder in each cup will weigh:

$\frac{1}{9} \times \frac{9}{10}$ lb. = _____

10. You have 2 dowels. One is $\frac{7}{8}$ in. thick. The second is $\frac{1}{2}$ as thick. How thick is the second dowel?

$\frac{1}{2} \times \frac{7}{8}$ in. = _____

35. Dividing Fractions

> **QUICK REMINDER**
>
> *How do you divide in a Life Skills problem such as $\frac{3}{4}$ yd. ÷ 3?*
>
> When you divide a number by 3, it's the same as taking $\frac{1}{3}$ of it.
>
> $\frac{3}{4}$ yd. ÷ 3 = $\frac{\cancel{3}^{1}}{4}$ yd. × $\frac{1}{\cancel{3}_{1}}$ = $\frac{1}{4}$ yd.

EXERCISES

1. How much is $\frac{3}{4}$ lb. ÷ 2? (Change the 2 into $\frac{1}{2}$ and multiply.)

   _____

2. How much is $\frac{5}{8}$ yd. ÷ 5?

   _____

3. How much is $\frac{3}{10}$ mile ÷ 2?

   _____

4. How much is $\frac{3}{16}$ in. ÷ 3?

   _____

5. How much is $\frac{2}{3}$ lb. ÷ 3?

   _____

6. How much is $2\frac{1}{2}$ lbs. ÷ 2? (First change $2\frac{1}{2}$ into $\frac{5}{2}$. Then change 2 into $\frac{1}{2}$ and multiply.)

   _____

7. How much is $3\frac{3}{4}$ yds. ÷ 3?

   _____

8. How much is $2\frac{1}{4}$ acres ÷ 4?

   _____

9. How much is $5\frac{1}{2}$ meters ÷ 6?

   _____

10. How much is $9\frac{1}{3}$ tons ÷ 3?

    _____

36. Review of Multiplying and Dividing Fractions

EXERCISES

1. $3 \times \frac{1}{16}$ in. = _____

2. $6 \times \frac{3}{4}$ lb. = _____
(Simplify your answers whenever you can.)

3. $9 \times \frac{2}{3}$ yd. = _____

4. You have a 15 lb. turkey. The cookbook tells you to cook it 20 minutes ($\frac{1}{3}$ hour) for each lb. How many hours should you cook the turkey?

$15 \times \frac{1}{3}$ hr. = _____

5. You work 20 hours per week. You are on your feet $\frac{3}{4}$ of this time. How many hours per week are you on your feet?

_____

6. $\frac{1}{3} \times \$3.36$ = _____

7. $\frac{3}{8} \times 200$ yds. = _____

8. $\frac{3}{7} \times \$49$ = _____

9. Roast beef costs \$4.50 per lb. How much is $\frac{2}{3}$ lb.?

_____

10. You are on your way to Denver. The trip is 720 mi. long. You have gone $\frac{3}{4}$ of the way. How far have you gone?

_____

11. $2\frac{1}{4} \times \$1.60$ = _____
(First change $2\frac{1}{4}$ to a regular fraction.)

12. $3\frac{3}{8} \times \$40$ = _____

13. $7\frac{1}{3} \times 12$ lbs. = _____

14. Plywood panels are 48 in. wide. You have $3\frac{1}{2}$ panels. How many in. wide are they altogether?

$3\frac{1}{2} \times 48$ in. = _____

15. You need 12 pieces of wire. Each piece is $2\frac{3}{4}$ in. long. How much wire do you need altogether?

_____

16. $\frac{2}{3} \times \frac{9}{10}$ meter = _____

17. $\frac{3}{4} \times \frac{3}{5}$ lb. = _____

18. $\frac{1}{5} \times \frac{3}{16}$ in. = _____

19. Your recipe calls for $\frac{2}{3}$ cup rice. You only want to make $\frac{1}{2}$ of the full recipe. How much rice will you need?

$\frac{1}{2} \times \frac{2}{3}$ cup = _____

20. You have $\frac{3}{4}$ lb. hamburger. You only want to use $\frac{1}{2}$ of it. How much hamburger will you use?

_____

21. How much is $\frac{9}{10}$ meter ÷ 3? (Change the 3 into $\frac{1}{3}$ and multiply.)

_____

22. How much is $\frac{7}{8}$ lb. ÷ 4?

_____

23. How much is $\frac{3}{4}$ ounce ÷ 5?

_____

24. How much is $3\frac{1}{8}$ in. ÷ 5? (First change $3\frac{1}{8}$ to a regular fraction. Then change 5 to $\frac{1}{5}$ and multiply.)

_____

25. How much is $3\frac{1}{3}$ mi. ÷ 4?

_____

Unit V.
LIFE SKILLS PERCENTS, DECIMALS, AND HUNDREDTHS

37. Percents, Decimals, and Hundredths—Introduction

38. Percents, Decimals, and Hundredths—Part 2

39. The Most Common Fractions, Percents, and Decimals

40. Adding and Subtracting Percents and Decimals

41. Multiplying by Decimals—In Life Skills Situations

42. Multiplying by Percents—In Life Skills Situations

43. Review of Percents, Decimals, and Hundredths

37. Percents, Decimals and Hundredths
—Introduction

EXERCISES

1. Which of these is <u>bigger</u>?
   Circle your answer.

   .07   .70

2. Which of these is bigger?
   .06   .6

3. Which of these is bigger?
   .33   .033

4. Which of these is bigger?
   .2   .02

5. Which of these is bigger?
   .078   .78

6. Match: (Draw lines connecting any that are equal.)

   .04 $\frac{4}{100}$

   .40 $\frac{40}{100}$

7. Match:

   .7 $\frac{7}{100}$

   .07 $\frac{70}{100}$

8. Five percent =
   .5%   5%   50%

9. Seventy-five percent =
   .75%   75%   7.5%

10. Which of these is biggest?
    .40   .04   .045

11. Which of these is biggest?
    .9   .09   .095

12. Which of these is biggest?
    .018   .18   .10

13. Which of these is biggest?
    .04   .045   .30

14. Which of these is biggest?
    .08   .2   .054

15. Which of these is biggest?
    .5   .08   .013

38. Percents, Decimals, Hundredths—Part II

EXERCISES

Fill in the missing numbers.

1. Eight percent =

   ——— %

   ——— (decimal)

   ——— (hundredths)

2. Twelve percent =

   ——— %

   ——— (decimal)

   ——— (hundredths)

3. Eighty percent =

   ——— %

   ——— (decimal)

   ——— (hundredths)

4. Two percent =

   ——— %

   ——— (decimal)

   ——— (hundredths)

5. .09 = ——— %

6. .90 = ——— %

7. .95 = ——— %

8. .3 = .30 = ——— %

9. .2 = .20 = ——— %

10. 50% =   .5   .05
    (Circle your answer)

11. 40% =   .4   .04

Fill in the missing number.

12. .7 = ——— %
    (Careful! This one is tricky!)

13. .15 = ——— %

14. .1 = ——— %

15. $\frac{55}{100}$ = ——— %

39. The Most Common Fractions, Percents, and Decimals

QUICK REMINDER

$\frac{1}{4}$ = .25 = 25% $\frac{3}{4}$ = .75 = 75% $\frac{2}{3}$ = .66 = 66 %

$\frac{1}{2}$ = .5 or .50 = 50% $\frac{1}{3}$ = .33 = 33 %

EXERCISES

Fill in the missing number.

1. $\frac{1}{4}$ ft. = —— ft. (decimal)

2. $\frac{1}{3}$ mi. = —— mi. (decimal)

3. $.75 = —— % of a dollar

4. $.50 = —— % of a dollar

5. 30% is bigger/smaller than $\frac{1}{3}$.

6. 68% is bigger/smaller than $\frac{2}{3}$.

7. 25% of the voters = —— (one of the most common fractions) of the voters

8. 50% of the budget = —— (fraction) of the budget

9. You have a calculator. You want to punch in $\frac{1}{2}$. What decimal do you punch? ——

10. You want to punch in $3\frac{1}{2}$. What decimal do you punch?

    3.1   3.2   3.5

11. You want to punch in $\frac{3}{4}$. What decimal do you punch? ——

12. You want to punch in $2\frac{1}{4}$. What decimal do you punch?

    2.1   2.2   2.25

40. Adding and Subtracting Percents and Decimals

EXERCISES

1. Add: 27% + 11%

```
  _____
+ _____
  _____
```

2. Subtract: 99% − 55%

3. Subtract: 68% − 4%

4. Add: 12% + 3% + 29%

5. Add: 25% + 30% + 41% + 6%

6. Add: .68 + .31

7. Add: .49 + .29

8. Subtract: .80 − .13

9. Subtract: .75 − .67

10. Add: .52 + .10

11. Add: .52 + .1
(Careful! This is tricky!
You will get it right if
you line up the decimal
points.)

13. Subtract: .70 − .3

15. Add: .06 + .4 + .789

14. Add: .15 + .22 + .305

12. Subtract: .70 − .31

41. Multiplying by Decimals —In Life Skills Situations

QUICK REMINDER

To multiply times a decimal, be sure to put the right number of decimal places in your answer.

```
  70 lbs.        There are 2 "decimal places" or numbers
×.25  ◄───────── after the decimal point in the number .25.
  3 50
14 0           Put the same number of decimal places
17.50 lbs. ◄─── in your answer.
```

EXERCISES

1. $300
       × .02

3.   1,350 acres
       × .25

4. Look at this part of a
sales slip:

SOLD BY	CASH	C. O. D.	CHARGE	ON ACCT.	MDSE. RETD.	PAID OUT	
QUAN.		DESCRIPTION				PRICE	AMOUNT
5		Sets A-621					295 —
					8% TAX		
						TOTAL	

What will the tax be?

Multiply: $295
          × .08

2.   5,500 lbs.
       × .33

5. Multiply: 805 yds. × .9

8. Multiply:
150,000 people × .4

10. Roberto also bought a new car. It cost $11,300. He also has to pay a 7% tax. How much is his tax?

6. Multiply: $1,500 × .55

9. Paula bought a new car for $9,500. She has to pay a tax of .07 × her purchase price. How much is the tax?

$9,500 × .07

7. Multiply:
13,000 gallons × .13

42. Multiplying by Percents —In Life Skills Situations

QUICK REMINDER

To multiply times a percent, first change the percent into a decimal: 5% = .05

$220 × 5% = $ 220
                × .05 ◄——— 2 decimal places
              ————————
              $11.00 ◄——— same number of decimal places in answer

EXERCISES

1. Multiply $150 × 20% (First change 20% to a decimal.)

$ _____

_____

$ _____

2. Multiply: $84 × 50%

3.   Multiply: $84 × 5%

4.   Multiply: 200 lbs. × 65%

5.   Multiply: 268 inches × 7%

6.   Multiply: 1,100 acres × 30%

7.   Multiply: 1,100 acres × 3%

8.   Martha was making $7 per hour. She just got a 13% raise. How much more money per hour will she make now?

$7 × 13% =

9.   Celina was making $9 per hour. She also just got a 13% raise. How much more money per hour will she make now?

_____

10. Sam wants to buy a coat. The price tag says $188. But there is a sale on, and the coat has been marked down 50%. It now costs only 50% of $188. How much is the sale price of the coat?

_____

43. Review of Percents, Decimals, and Hundredths

EXERCISES

1. Which of these is bigger? (Circle your answer.)

   .90   .09

2. Which of these is bigger?

   .8   .08

3. Which of these is bigger?

   .03   .015

4. Match:

   .06 $\dfrac{6}{100}$

   .6 $\dfrac{60}{100}$

5. Eight percent =

   ——— %

   ——— (decimal)

   ——— (hundredths)

6. Forty-eight percent =

   ——— %

   ——— (decimal)

   ——— (hundredths)

7. Which of the following = $\dfrac{90}{100}$? (Circle your answer.)

   .09   .9   .090

8. Which of the following = 90%?

   .09   .9   .090

9. .23 = ——— %

10. .2 = ——— %

11. $\dfrac{1}{2}$ acre =

    ——— acre (decimal)

12. $66\dfrac{2}{3}\%$ =

    ——— (one of the most common fractions)

13. .75 =

    ——— (common fraction)

14. $.33\dfrac{1}{3}$ =

    ——— (common fraction)

15. Sandra wants to punch in $\dfrac{1}{4}$ on her calculator.

    What decimal does she punch?

    ———

16. Add: 51% + 20%

17. Add: 35% + 7%

18. Subtract: 98% − 40%

19. Subtract: 98% − 4%

20. Add:
    40% + 16% + 5% + 9%

21. Add: .33 + .39

22. Add: .66 + .2

23. Subtract: .85 − .09

24. Subtract: .64 − .3

25. Add: .35 + .48 + .1 + .08

26. $282
        × .06

27. 400 miles
        × .75

28. 400 miles
        × .5

29. Multiply: 3,500 yds. × .3

30. You just bought a house for $50,000. You have to pay a sales commission of .05. How much is the commission in dollars?

_____

31. Multiply: $660 × 12%. (First change the 12% to a decimal.)

32. Multiply: 990 liters × 40%

33. Multiply: $702 × 5%

34. Multiply: $8 × 15%

35. You sold your used car for $2,750. You have to pay a 2% transfer tax. How much is the transfer tax in dollars?

Unit VI.
LIFE SKILLS
WORD PROBLEMS

---

44. Real World Problems—Add or Subtract?

45. Real World Problems—Multiply or Divide?

46. Real World Problems—With More than One Step

47. Real World Problems—Do You Have the Right Information?

48. Price and Cost Comparisons

49. Price and Cost Comparisons—Part 2

50. Unit Pricing

51. Review of Life Skills Word Problems

44. Real World Problems—Add or Subtract?

EXERCISES

1. Brand X costs $9.79 each. Brand Y costs $7.99. What is the difference in price?

   ☐ add   ☐ subtract

2. Package A weighs 3.24 lbs. Package B weighs 4.65 lbs. How much more does package B weigh?

   ☐ add   ☐ subtract

3. The last time we paid $19 per dozen. Now the price is $27.20 per dozen. How big was the increase? (Think of it as how big is the difference, or how much more?)

   ☐ add   ☐ subtract

4. You bought pencils for $2.05 and paper for $1.89. Tax was $.12. How much did you pay in total?

   ☐ add   ☐ subtract

5. If you fly on the tour special, it will cost $240. If you fly regular tourist class, it will cost $355. How much extra does it cost to fly tourist class?

   ☐ add   ☐ subtract

6. The bill was $13.25. You gave the clerk $20. How much change should you get?

   ☐ add   ☐ subtract

7. First weigh each of these 3 packages. Then tell me how much they weigh altogether.

   ☐ add   ☐ subtract

8. You worked 3 hours painting your apartment on Sunday, $4\frac{1}{2}$ hours on Monday, and 2 hours yesterday. How long did you spend in total?

   ☐ add   ☐ subtract

9. You used $1\frac{1}{2}$ gallons of paint for the kitchen and 3 gallons for the bedroom. How much paint did both rooms take together?

   ☐ add   ☐ subtract

10. Make up a bill for these 4 items. Then give me a total.

    ☐ add   ☐ subtract

45. Real World Problems—Multiply or Divide?

QUICK REMINDER

Multiply when—
All items are the same (size, weight, or price, for example);
you know how many; you want a total.

Example: You pack 12 kits to a carton. You are supposed to pack
150 cartons. How many kits in total will you pack?
(To find out, you multiply.)

Divide when—
You want to figure out an average amount.
Or: All items are the same (size, weight, price); you know the total;
you want to know how many (or how much).

Example: You are driving to Boston. The trip is 2,500 miles.
You'll average 500 miles per day. How many days will it take?
(To find out, you divide.)

EXERCISES

1. You bought root beer on special—24 cans
   for $3.60. How much did each can cost?

   ☐ multiply   ☐ divide

2. You earn $40 per day. In 5 days, how much
   do you earn altogether?

   ☐ multiply   ☐ divide

3. The publisher shipped you a carton of
   books. It weighs 40 lbs. There are 80 Life
   Skills Math books in it. How much does
   each book weigh?

   ☐ multiply   ☐ divide

4. You were on vacation for 8 days. The holiday
   cost you $1,200. What did it cost you on the
   average for each day?

   ☐ multiply   ☐ divide

5. It costs Lennie $1.50 per day in bus fare to go
   to work and come home. To figure out his
   weekly cost, he should multiply times 5 (the
   number of days he works per week).

   ☐ true   ☐ false

6. You want to figure out your average daily
   expenses for groceries. To do so, you divide
   your weekly expenses by 7 (the number of
   days in a week).

   ☐ true   ☐ false

7. You know your monthly rent. How do you figure
   out your yearly rent?

   ☐ multiply by 12   ☐ divide by 12

8. You know how many miles you drove last year.
   How do you figure out how many miles on the
   average you drove each month?

   ☐ multiply by 12   ☐ divide by 12

9. You drove 70 miles on 10 liters of gas. How
   many miles per liter did you average?

   ☐ multiply   ☐ divide

10. You want to ship out 75 cartons of goods. Each
    carton weighs 20 kilograms. How much do
    the 75 cartons weigh in total?

    ☐ multiply   ☐ divide

46. Real World Problems
—With More Than One Step

EXERCISES

1. You have picked out $2\frac{1}{2}$ kilograms of pears at $.79 per kilogram and a melon for $1.59. What is the total cost for the pears and melon together? (Hint: Multiply, to find cost of pears. Then add.)

   _____

2. You and a friend have gotten some new things for your apartment. Dishes cost $18.95. A dish rack cost $6.95. Hand towels cost $3. You want to split the cost evenly. How much do you each owe? (Hint: Add. Then divide by 2.)

   _____

3. You got sick and had to go to the doctor. It cost $50 for the doctor, $55 for blood tests, and $19 for medicine. Your health plan will pay 80% of the total. How much will the health plan pay? (Hint: Add. Then multiply times 80%.)

   _____

4. You are comparing 2 kinds of plastic sheets. One kind weighs 1.5 lbs. per sheet. The other kind weighs 24 lbs. for a bundle of 12 sheets. Which kind weighs more on the average? (Hint: Find average weight of second kind. Then compare.)

   _____

5. <u>Cost of Car A</u>: $7,400 + $600 for extras + $400 tax.

   <u>Cost of Car B</u>: $9,000 for everything together (including tax) <u>minus</u> a 10% discount the company is offering.

   Which costs more? (<u>Hint</u>: Add for Car A. Multiply times 90%—what you will pay after discount—for Car B. Then compare.)

   _____

6. You sell magazines. You made $28 on Wednesday and $35 on Thursday. You worked ten hours on both days together. How much did you earn per hour on the average?

   _____

7. Carla worked 4 hours on Monday, 3 hours on Thursday and 8 hours on Saturday. She gets $4.20 per hour. How much is she owed in total for all 3 days?

   _____

8. To make a bed, you need 2 lengths of board 6 feet long and 2 other lengths 4 feet long. The boards cost $1.25 per running foot. How many feet in total for the 4 boards? And what is the total cost? (<u>Hint</u>: Multiply 2 × 6 ft. and 2 × 4 ft. Then add. Then multiply.)

   _____

9. Melanie is a jogger. She jogged 2 miles on Monday, 4 miles on Wednesday, and 3 miles on Friday. What was the <u>average</u> number of miles she jogged each day?

   _____

10. Melanie averages 9 minutes per mile. How much time did she spend running for the 3 days altogether?

   _____

47. Real World Problems
—Do You Have The Right Information?

QUICK REMINDER

Sometimes you don't have enough information.

Example: Alonso plans to tune up his car. He plans to buy a tune-up kit for $6.99 and spark plugs for $1.49 each. How much in total will it cost him for parts?
    You don't know how many spark plugs there are.

Sometimes you have more information than you need.

Example: Patricia built some bookcases. She paid $60 for lumber. She worked 2 hours on Tuesday, $1\frac{1}{2}$ hours on Friday, and another $1\frac{1}{2}$ hours on Saturday. How much time did she work altogether?
    The cost of lumber doesn't help at all in this problem.

EXERCISES

1. You'll need 3 gallons of paint at $10.99 per gallon, and a paint roller set for $8.99. You'll also need some paint thinner.

   "How much cash will I need?"

   ☐ not enough information
   ☐ more information than you need
   ☐ just the right information

2. Your flight leaves at 8:05 AM. It will take an hour to get to the airport. And you should be there 45 minutes before flight time.

   "When should I leave?"

   ☐ not enough information
   ☐ more information than you need
   ☐ just the right information

3. When it's 9:00 AM in New York, it's 8:00 AM in Chicago, and 7:00 AM in Denver, and 6:00 AM in Los Angeles.

   How many hours difference is there between New York and Los Angeles?

   ☐ not enough information
   ☐ more information than you need
   ☐ just the right information

4. Janet is paid a commission on her sales. She gets a certain amount for each dollar she sells.

   Her sales last week were $1,100. How much did she make in commission?

   ☐ not enough information
   ☐ more information than you need
   ☐ just the right information

5. You go to work at 7:30 AM, take an hour off for lunch, and leave at 2:30 in the afternoon. How many total hours do you work?

   ☐ not enough information
   ☐ more information than you need
   ☐ just the right information

6. The temperature at 8 PM was 75 degrees. During the night the temperature dropped 28 degrees. What was the low temperature?

   ☐ not enough information
   ☐ more information than you need
   ☐ just the right information

7. "How much do you want for the hi-fi?"

"I paid $500 for it. I'll sell it to you for half. And that chair over there cost me $75 and the sofa cost $650 on special."

☐ not enough information
☐ nore information than you need
☐ just the right information

8. Pedro swam 50 laps of the pool. How far did he swim altogether?

☐ not enough information
☐ more information than you need
☐ just the right information

9. One strip of copper is 3 millimeters thick. The second is 4.8 millimeters thick. They are each 20 millimeters long.

How thick are the 2 strips together?

☐ not enough information
☐ more information than you need
☐ just the right information

10. You bought 3 boxes of file folders at $10.80 per box and 40 pads of paper. The paper was at a special price.

What did you pay altogether?

☐ not enough information
☐ more information than you need
☐ just the right information

48. Price and Cost Comparisons

QUICK REMINDER

Which is cheaper per can?

Step 1. Find the price per can of the Napoli brand.

Divide 3 into $1.00 = $.33$\frac{1}{3}$ = $.34 per can.

(The store will even off to the next higher cent.)

Step 2. Compare.

SUPER-O TOMATO PASTE   Napoli TOMATO PASTE

39¢   3/$1.00

EXERCISES

1. Bathroom tissues   Bathroom tissues
   $.49 per roll   2 rolls for $.85

   Which bathroom tissue is cheaper per roll?

   ☐ $.49 per roll   ☐ 2/$.85

2. Tube socks   Tube socks
   $.69 each   6/$4.80

   Which is cheaper per pair of tube socks?

   ☐ $.69   ☐ 6/$4.80

80

3. **Ice cream**
   Pint—$1.49   Ice Cream
                 Quart (2 pints)—$2.49

   Which ice cream is cheaper per pint?
   ☐ Pint—$1.49   ☐ Quart—$2.49

4. **Spaghetti**
   8 oz.—$.39   Spaghetti
                 16 oz.—$.73

   Which spaghetti is cheaper per 8 oz.?
   (Figure 16 oz. is twice as much as 8 oz.)
   ☐ 8 oz.—$.39   ☐ 16 oz.—$.73

5. **Bars of soap**
   25¢ each   Bars of soap
               4/$.89

   Which soap is cheaper per bar?
   ☐ 25¢ each   ☐ 4/$.89

6. **Bacon**
   $\frac{1}{2}$ lb.—$1.49   Bacon
                              1 lb.—$2.49

   Which bacon is cheaper per $\frac{1}{2}$ lb.?
   ☐ $\frac{1}{2}$ lb.—$1.49   ☐ 1 lb.—$2.49

7. **Coffee mugs**
   $3 each   Coffee mugs
              6/$9

   Which is cheaper per coffee mug?
   ☐ $3 each   ☐ 6/$9

8. **Brand X coffee**
   1 lb. for $2.99   Brand Y coffee
                      3 lbs. for $9.79

   Which coffee is cheaper per lb.?
   ☐ Brand X   ☐ Brand Y

9. **Carrots**
   39¢/lb.   Carrots
              3 lbs. for $1.49

   Which carrots are cheaper per lb.?
   ☐ 39¢/lb.   ☐ 3 lbs. for $1.49

10. **Corn**
    20¢ per ear   Corn
                   6 ears for $.99

    Which corn is cheaper per ear?
    ☐ 20¢ per ear   ☐ 6/$.99

49. Price and Cost Comparisons—Part II

EXERCISES

1. Brand X   Brand Y
   Dog Food   Dog Food
   4 lbs. for $2.59 5 lbs. for $2.79

   Which is cheaper per lb.?

   ☐ Brand X   ☐ Brand Y

2. Garbage Bags   Garbage Bags
   20 for $1.59   30 for $2.09

   Which is cheaper per garbage bag?

   ☐ 20 for $1.59   ☐ 30 for $2.09

3. Soda   Soda
   24 oz. for $.79   36 oz. for $.89

   Which soda is cheaper per ounce?

   ☐ 24 oz. for $.79   ☐ 36 oz. for $.89

4. Tomato juice   Tomato juice
   46 oz. for $.99   "6 pack"—6 6-oz.
                     cans for $.99

   Which tomato juice is cheaper per ounce?
   (First find total number of ounces in 6-pack.)

   ☐ 46 oz. for $.99   ☐ 6-pack

5. Pound cake   Pound cake
   9 oz. for $1.29   11 oz. for $1.19

   Which pound cake is cheaper per ounce?

   ☐ 9 oz. for $1.29   ☐ 11 oz. for $1.19

6. Plastic bottles Plastic bottles
   1,000 for $180   2,000 for $320

   Which is cheaper per bottle?

   ☐ 1,000 for $180   ☐ 2,000 for $320

7. Cream cheese   Cream cheese
   3 oz. for $.39   8 oz. for $.88

   Which cream cheese is cheaper per ounce?

   ☐ 3 oz. for $.39   ☐ 8 oz. for $.88

8. Brand X   Brand Y
   Instant Coffee   Instant Coffee
   6 oz. for $4.19   10 oz. for $5.79

   Which instant coffee is cheaper per oz.?

   ☐ Brand X   ☐ Brand Y

9. Tea bags
16 for $.59

Tea bags
48 for $.99

Which is cheaper per tea bag?

☐ 16 for $.59   ☐ 48 for $.99

10. Brand X
Toothpaste
7 oz. for $1.39

Brand Y
Toothpaste
9 oz. for $2.09

Which toothpaste is cheaper per ounce?

☐ Brand X   ☐ Brand Y

11. Frozen fried chicken
28 oz. for $3.79

Frozen fried chicken
32 oz. for $3.89

Which fried chicken is cheaper per ounce?

☐ 28 oz. for $3.79   ☐ 32 oz. for $3.89

12. Detergent
35 oz. for $1.39

Detergent
50 oz. for $2.49

Which detergent is cheaper per ounce?

☐ 35 oz. for $1.39   ☐ 50 oz. for $2.49

13. Frozen waffles
10 oz. for $.89

Frozen waffles
14 oz. for $.98

Which frozen waffles are cheaper per oz.?

☐ 10 oz. for $.89   ☐ 14 oz. for $.98

14. Aspirin
50 tablets for $.96

Aspirin
100 tablets for $2.99

Which aspirin is cheaper per tablet?

☐ 50 for $.96   ☐ 100 for $2.99

15. Cooking oil
16 oz. for $.96

Cooking oil
24 oz. for $1.19

Which cooking oil is cheaper per oz.?

☐ 16 oz. for $.96   ☐ 24 oz. for $1.19

83

50. Unit Pricing

QUICK REMINDER

When items have unit pricing labels, it is easy to compare prices.
You just have to pick out the right numbers.

NET WT. LBS.	PRICE PER LB.	YOU PAY
0.98	2.69	2.64

A. Porterhouse Steak

NET WT LBS	PRICE PER LB.	YOU PAY
0.92	2.79	2.53

B. T-Bone Steak

The Porterhouse steak is cheaper <u>per pound</u>—only $2.69.

EXERCISES

1.

SOUR CREAM		
Net weight	Price per lb.	You pay
8 oz.	$1.34	$.67

What is the price per pound of sour cream?

_____

What price do you pay for the 8-oz. ($\frac{1}{2}$ pound)

container? _____

2. Whole wheat bread—12 ounces

Unit Price 76.0¢ per lb.	You Pay 57¢ for 12-oz. loaf

What is the price per lb. of this loaf of bread?

_____

What price do you pay? _____
How many ounces are there in this loaf?

_____

3. Reconstituted lemon juice—16 fluid ounces

Unit Price $1.98 per quart (32 fl. oz.)	You Pay $.99 for 16 fl. oz.

What price do you pay for the bottle of

lemon juice? _____
How many ounces are in the bottle? _____

4.

APPLE JUICE—32 fl. oz.	
Unit Price 93¢/qt.	You Pay 93¢

What is the unit price (per qt.)? _____

What price do you pay? _____

5. Lamb chops

Net wt.	TOTAL	Price per lb.
0.96 lbs.	$3.06	$3.19

What is the price per lb. of lamb chops?

_____

How many lbs. in this package?   _____

How much in total do you pay for the package?

_____

6.

SHREDDED WHEAT—10 oz.	
Price per lb.	You Pay
$1.17	$.73

Match:

$1.17   Unit price

$ .73   Price of package

7.

CURRANT JELLY—12 oz.	
Unit Price	You Pay
$1.11/lb.	$.83

What is the price per pound of this jelly?

_____

8. Copper pan cleaners—3 in package

Unit Price	You Pay
$28.3 ea.	$.85

How many cleaners in this package?   _____

What is the unit price per pan cleaner?

_____

9. Baby shampoo—16 fl. oz.

Unit Price	You Pay
$2.98/qt.	$1.49

What is the price of this bottle of shampoo?

_____

How many fluid ounces does it contain?

_____

10. American cheese—12 oz.

12 oz. for $1.69
Unit Price—$2.25 per lb. (16 oz.)

What is the price per lb. of this cheese?

_____

What is the price of the package?   _____

51. Review of Life Skills Word Problems

EXERCISES

1. "What is the total weight on those 3 packages? The first weighs 2.7 kilograms. The second weighs 4.36 kilograms. And the third weighs 8.1 kilograms."

   ☐ add ☐ multiply
   ☐ subtract ☐ divide

2. "Next give me the total weight of these 6 packages. They are all the same. They each weigh 5.5 kilograms."

   ☐ add ☐ multiply
   ☐ subtract ☐ divide

3. The price of the calculator is $12.99. Tax is $.91. How much does the calculator cost altogether?

   ☐ add ☐ multiply
   ☐ subtract ☐ divide

4. The total price of the calculator in question is $13.90 with tax. The price of a better model is $17.11 with tax. How much extra does the second model cost?

   ☐ add ☐ multiply
   ☐ subtract ☐ divide

5. When you started on your vacation, your car had 29,305 miles on it. At the end of the vacation, the mileage indicator showed 32,058 miles. How many miles did you drive during your vacation?

   ☐ add ☐ multiply
   ☐ subtract ☐ divide

6. You drove 2,753 miles in 9 days. How many miles per day did you average?

   ☐ add ☐ multiply
   ☐ subtract ☐ divide

7. Giacomo drinks an average of $1\frac{1}{2}$ pints of milk per day. How much milk does he drink in a full year?

   ☐ add ☐ multiply
   ☐ subtract ☐ divide

8. June is taking yoga classes. She pays $56 for 16 classes. What does each class cost her?

   ☐ add ☐ multiply
   ☐ subtract ☐ divide

9. Larry is a swimmer. He swims in a pool that is 50 meters wide. There are 1,500 meters in a mile.

   How many widths of the pool does Larry have to swim to cover a mile? (Figure this one out and write your answer below.)

   _____

10. It takes Larry an average of 2 minutes to swim 1 lap. About how long does it take him to swim 45 laps? (Figure it out.)

_____

11. Mischa is on a diet. He keeps track of the calories in each meal he eats. For breakfast he had:

   2 boiled eggs (80 calories in each egg)
   1 slice of whole wheat toast (55 calories)
   A cup of tea with lemon (5 calories)
   An orange (75 calories)

How many calories were there altogether in his breakfast?

_____

12. Trina is shopping for a stereo set. The 2 speakers she wants cost $140 each. The receiver costs $220. The turntable costs $160.

The store will give her 10% off if she buys everything together. How many dollars savings is this? (Figure the cost of the 4 items. Then multiply by 10%.)

$ _____

13. Arnie wants to go to Boston. A round trip by train from where Arnie lives usually costs $23 each way. But if he travels at special times of the week, he can get a round trip ticket for only $28.

How much will he save if he buys the special round trip fare, instead of 2 regular fares?

_____

14. You are thinking of joining a book club. You would get 4 books for $1 apiece. But then you would have to buy 4 more books. These 4 books would cost an average of $10 apiece.

How much would all 8 books cost?

_____

15. Look at your answer to the last question. It tells you how much all 8 books would cost.

What would the average cost of each book be?

_____

16. Jill works in an office. She is entitled to take 2 sick days off with full pay for every 3 months she works.

How many paid sick days does she get in a year?

_____

17. Selina is a jogger. She knows it takes her about 8 minutes on the average for each mile she jogs.

Suppose she runs 40 minutes. About how many miles will she cover?

_____

18. Martia wants to call Fresno, California. It costs 54¢ for the first minute and 38¢ for each minute after that.

What does a 5-minute call cost?

_____

19. If Martia calls after 5 in the afternoon, it costs only 35¢ for the first minute and 24¢ for each minute after that.

What would a 5-minute call cost after 5 P.M.?

_____

20. Compare your answers to questions 18 and 19.

How much would Martia save on a 5-minute call by waiting until after 5 P.M.?

_____

21. Pamela had a Xerox place run off 15 copies of her resume. The first 5 copies cost $.10 each. The next 10 copies cost $.06 each. In addition, she had to pay 5% tax.

How much did the 15 copies cost her in total?

_____

22. Randy takes a bus to work. The bus ride takes 20 minutes. But Randy also has to walk from his house to the bus stop, and from the place where the bus lets him off to his job. Besides, he usually has about a 10 minute wait for the bus. And he likes to give himself 15 minutes leeway in case the bus is late.

How much time in total should he set aside for going to work in the morning?

- [ ] not enough information
- [ ] more information than you need
- [ ] just the right information

23. Marusha put a roll of film in her camera and took pictures of her dog. She used the whole roll of film. Then she took the film to the photo lab. It costs 45¢ for each print the lab makes from the film.

How much in total will it cost Marusha to have prints made from her roll of film?

- [ ] not enough information
- [ ] more information than you need
- [ ] just the right information

24. Lennie bought traveler's checks for his vacation so he wouldn't have to carry around so much cash. The fee was $1\frac{1}{2}$% of the amount of his purchase. He bought $500 worth. He also took $250 in cash with him. But he used $93 of that to pay for his ticket.

How much was the fee?

- [ ] not enough information
- [ ] more information than you need
- [ ] just the right information

25.
Brand X Frozen Orange Juice Concentrate (6 oz.) $.67 ea.	Brand Y Frozen Orange Juice Concentrate (6 oz.) 3/$1.49

Which orange juice is cheaper per can?

- [ ] Brand X
- [ ] Brand Y

26.
Brand X Margarine 89¢/lb.	Brand Y Margarine 2 lbs. for $1.89

Which margarine is cheaper per pound?

- [ ] Brand X
- [ ] Brand Y

27. Store A — Records—$5.98 each   Store B — Records—2 for $12.98

Which store sells individual records cheaper?

- [ ] Store A
- [ ] Store B

28. Baked beans 49¢ per can   Baked beans 3 cans/$1.19

Which baked beans are cheaper per can?

- [ ] 49¢ per can
- [ ] 3/$1.19

29. Corn flakes 12 oz. for $.65   Corn flakes 18 oz. for $.95

Which corn flakes are cheaper per ounce?

- [ ] 12 oz. for $.65
- [ ] 18 oz. for $.95

30. Snack crackers 10 oz. for $.99   Snack crackers 16 oz. for $1.29

Which snack crackers are cheaper per ounce?

- [ ] 10 oz. for $.99
- [ ] 16 oz. for $1.29

31.
Brand X Swiss Cheese 6 ounces for $1.49	Brand Y Swiss Cheese 8 ounces for $2.19

Which Swiss cheese is cheaper per ounce?

- [ ] Brand X
- [ ] Brand Y

32.
Brand X Apple Pie 26 ounces for $1.30	Brand Y Apple Pie 31 ounces for $2.17

Which apple pie is cheaper per ounce?

- [ ] Brand X
- [ ] Brand Y

33.

SHELL STEAK		
Net wt. lbs.	Price per lb.	You Pay
1.03 lbs.	$4.29	$4.40

What is the cost of this package of shell steak?

$ —————

What is the price per pound? $ —————

34. Which peanut butter is cheaper per lb.?

☐ Brand X   ☐ Brand Y

Brand X Peanut Butter 12 oz.—95¢ Unit Price: $1.27/lb.

Brand Y Peanut Butter 1 lb.—$1.19

35. Bleach—64 fluid ounces

Unit Price	You Pay
31.5¢/Quart (32 fl. oz.)	$.63

How many fluid ounces in this container

of bleach? —————

What is the price per quart? —————

What is the price for the container? —————

Unit VII.
STANDARD MEASURES

52. Inches, Feet, and Yards

53. Square Inches

54. Square Feet and Square Yards

55. Ounces and Pounds

56. Fluid Ounces, Pints, Quarts, and Gallons

57. Metric Measures—Millimeters, Centimeters, and Kilometers

58. Metric Measures—Liters and Kilograms

59. Review of Standard Measures

52. Inches, Feet, and Yards

> **QUICK REMINDER**
>
> 12 inches (in.) = 1 foot (ft.)
> 3 ft. = 1 yard (yd.)

EXERCISES

1. 24 in. = —————— (how many?) ft.

2. 6 in. = ———— (fraction) ft.

3. Celia is 60 in. tall. How many <u>feet</u> tall is she?

————————

4. Celia's sister Annette is 66 in. tall. Turn her height into feet <u>and</u> inches.

———— ft. + ———— in.

5. 15 ft. = ———— (how many?) yds. (divide)

6. 10 yds. = ———— (how many?) ft. (multiply)

7. 8 ft. = ———— (how many?) in. (multiply)

8. A football field is 100 yds. long. How many feet long is it? ————

9. One mile is 5,280 ft. How many yards are in one mile? ————

10. Sung is 70 in. tall, and still growing. How many inches must he grow before he is 6 ft. tall?

————————

53. Square Inches

EXERCISES

1.
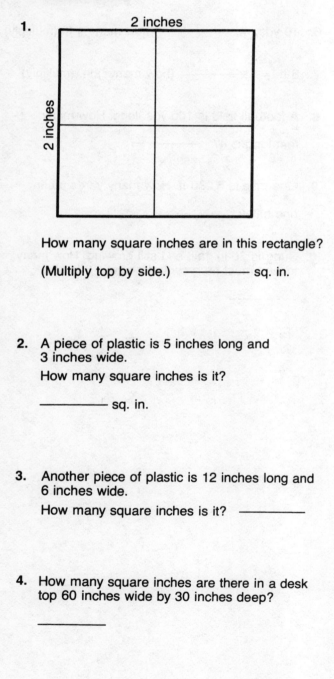
2 inches

2 inches

How many square inches are in this rectangle?

(Multiply top by side.) ———— sq. in.

2. A piece of plastic is 5 inches long and 3 inches wide.

   How many square inches is it?

   ———— sq. in.

3. Another piece of plastic is 12 inches long and 6 inches wide.

   How many square inches is it? ————

4. How many square inches are there in a desk top 60 inches wide by 30 inches deep?

   ————

5. Many books are 6 inches along the top and 9 inches along the side.

   How many square inches is one of these books?

   ————

6. Rectangle A   Rectangle B
   7 in. by 4 in.   8 in. by 3 in.

   Which has more sq. in.?

   ☐ Rectangle A   ☐ Rectangle B

7. Rectangle A   Rectangle B
   15 in. by 1 in.   9 in. by 3 in.

   Which has more sq. in.?

   ☐ Rectangle A   ☐ Rectangle B

8. Rectangle A   Rectangle B
   27 in. by 2 in.   12 in. by 10 in.

   Which has more sq. in.?

   ☐ Rectangle A   ☐ Rectangle B

9. Rectangle A   Rectangle B
   3 in. by 3 in.   4 in. by 2 in.

   Which has more sq. in.?

   ☐ Rectangle A   ☐ Rectangle B

10. Rectangle A   Rectangle B
    5 in. by 5 in.   6 in. by 4 in.

    Which has more sq. in.?

    ☐ Rectangle A   ☐ Rectangle B

54. Square Feet and Square Yards

QUICK REMINDER

*To figure out how many square feet or square yards in a rectangle,
multiple length by width.*

BUT: Remember you can't multiply **yards** by **feet.** When you have a
problem like this, first change the yards to feet (1 yd. = 3 ft.).
Or change feet to yards (3 ft. = 1 yd.)—Whichever is easier.

EXERCISES

1. The ceiling you want to paint is 15 feet long
by 14 feet wide.

   How many square feet is it?

   _____

2. The floor you want to refinish is 18 ft. by 10 ft.
   How many sq. ft. is it? _____

3. How many sq. yds. are in a field that is

   100 yds. by 50 yds.? _____

4. How many sq. ft. are in a rug 7 ft. by 9 ft.?

   _____

5. How big is a terrace 5 yds. long by 8 ft. wide?
   (First change yds. to ft., then multiply.)

   _____

6. How big is a surface 10 yds. by 9 ft.? (This
   time, change 9 ft. to 3 yds.)

   _____

7. The lawn you're working on is 25 yards long
   and 20 yards wide.

   How many square yards is the lawn?

   _____

8. Floor A   Floor B
   13 ft. × 10 ft.   15 ft. × 8 ft.

   Which has the bigger surface?

   ☐ Floor A   ☐ Floor B

9. The rug shampoo you bought will clean
   120 sq. ft. of rug surface.

   Will it clean a rug 9 ft. by 12 ft.?

   ☐ yes   ☐ no

10. The gallon of paint you bought will cover
    400 sq. ft. of wall surface.

    Will it cover a wall 20 ft. by 15 ft.?

    ☐ yes   ☐ no

55. Ounces and Pounds

QUICK REMINDER

16 ounces (oz.) = 1 pound (lb.)

EXERCISES

1. How many ounces are there in 2 pounds?

   _____

2. How many oz. are there in $\frac{1}{4}$ lb.?

   _____

3. How many oz. are in 5 lbs.?

   _____

4. 8 oz. = _____ (fraction) lb.

5. 12 oz. = _____ (fraction) lb.

6. Package A   Package B
   9 oz. ham $\frac{1}{2}$ lb. ham
   Which is bigger?
   ☐ Package A   ☐ Package B

7. Package A   Package B
   13 oz. pizza   1 lb. pizza
   Which is bigger?
   ☐ Package A   ☐ Package B

8. A package of meat is 24 oz.
   How many lbs. is it?

   _____

9. Can A   Can B
   Chili with beans   Chili with beans
   15 oz.—$.89   1 lb.—$.89
   Which is cheaper per oz.?
   ☐ Can A   ☐ Can B

10. You want to mail a $2\frac{1}{2}$ lb. package.
    How many ounces is the package?

    _____

94

56. Fluid Ounces, Pints, Quarts, and Gallons

QUICK REMINDER

2 tablespoons = 1 fluid ounce (fl. oz.)
8 fluid ounces = 1 cup
2 cups = 1 pint (pt.)
2 pints = 1 quart (qt.)
4 quarts = 1 gallon (gal.)

EXERCISES

1. You measured out 4 tablespoons of cooking oil.
   How many fl. oz. was that?

   _____

2. You measured out 2 cups of milk.
   How many fl. oz. was that?

   _____

3. You used 8 quarts of oil.
   How many gallons did you use?

   _____

4. You bought 2 pints of strawberries.
   How many quarts did you buy?

   _____

5. You bought $\frac{1}{2}$ gal. of milk.
   How many quarts did you buy?

   _____

6. Which of these = 1 quart?
   (Check more than one.)
   ☐ 32 fl. oz.
   ☐ 4 cups
   ☐ 2 pts.
   ☐ $\frac{1}{4}$ gal.

7. Bottle A   Bottle B   Bottle C
   16 fl. oz.   32 fl. oz.   64 fl. oz.
   Which of these = 1 quart?
   ☐ Bottle A   ☐ Bottle B   ☐ Bottle C

8. Bottle A   Bottle B   Bottle C
   16 fl. oz.   32 fl. oz.   64 fl. oz.
   Which of these = 1 gallon?
   ☐ Bottle A   ☐ Bottle B   ☐ Bottle C

9. Which of these = $\frac{1}{2}$ pint?
   (Check more than one.)
   ☐ 16 tablespoons   ☐ 8 fluid ounces   ☐ 1 cup

10. Container A   Container B
    1 quart milk $\frac{1}{2}$ gal. milk
    $.68 $1.49
    Which is cheaper per quart?
    ☐ Container A   ☐ Container B

57. Metric Measures—Millimeters, Centimeters, and Kilometers

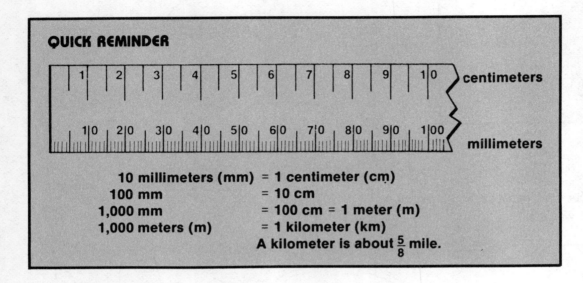

QUICK REMINDER

10 millimeters (mm) = 1 centimeter (cm)
100 mm   = 10 cm
1,000 mm   = 100 cm = 1 meter (m)
1,000 meters (m) = 1 kilometer (km)
A kilometer is about $\frac{5}{8}$ mile.

EXERCISES

1. _____

The line above is 3 cm long.
How many millimeters is it?

_____

2. _____

This line is 60 mm long.
How many cm is it?

_____

3. 1 meter = 39.37 inches, or a little more than—
☐ 1 foot   ☐ 1 yard

4. 3 meters = ——— (how many?) centimeters.

5. Mark is 2 m tall.
How many cm tall is he?

_____

6. A kilometer is about $\frac{5}{8}$ mile.
About how many miles is 8 km?

_____

7. Which is a faster rate of speed?
☐ 55 miles per hour   ☐ 55 km per hour

8. 80 km per hour = ——— (about how many?)
miles per hour.

9. Put these lengths in order (smallest to largest):
1 km   150 m   1,000 cm
_____ smallest

_____ middle

_____ largest

10. Match: (Draw lines to connect the ones that go together.)

1 m   less than $\frac{1}{2}$ in.

1 km   a few inches more than 1 yd.

10 mm   about $\frac{5}{8}$ mile

58. Metric Measures—Liters and Kilograms

EXERCISES

1. 4 liters = a little more than ——— quart(s)

2. 4 liters = about ——— gallon(s)

3. Which is larger?
   ☐ 5 gallons   ☐ 10 liters
   (Remember: 4 quarts = 1 gallon)

4. Which is larger?
   ☐ 10 liters   ☐ 10 quarts

5. Brand A   Brand B
   Cola   Cola
   1 liter $.89   1 quart $.89
   Which brand gives you more for your money?
   ☐ Brand A   ☐ Brand B

6. 1 lb. =
   ☐ about $\frac{1}{2}$ kg
   ☐ about $\frac{3}{4}$ kg
   ☐ about 1 kg

7. 5 lbs. =
   ☐ about 1 kg
   ☐ about 2 kg
   ☐ about 4 kg

8. Which is bigger?
   ☐ 5 lbs. of ham
   ☐ 5 kg of ham

9. Which is bigger?
   ☐ 5 lbs. of potatoes
   ☐ 5 kg of potatoes

10. Which is bigger?
    ☐ 10 lbs. of onions
    ☐ 5 kg of onions

59. Review of Standard Measures

EXERCISES

1. 1 yd. equals:

   ——— inches

   ——— feet

2. 72 in. = ——— (how many?) ft.

3. 100 yds. = ——— (how many?) ft.

4. Change 100 inches into feet and inches.

   ——— ft. + ——— in.

5.

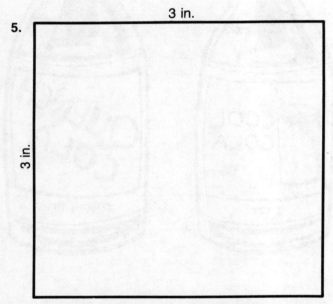

3 in.

3 in.

How many square inches in the figure above?

_____

6. How many sq. in. in 1 sq. ft.?
   (Remember: 1 sq. ft. is 12 in. × 12 in.)

   _____

7. Rectangle A   Rectangle B
   6 in. by 6 in.   7 in. by 4 in.

   Which has more sq. in.?

   ☐ Rectangle A   ☐ Rectangle B

8. The piece of wood paneling you bought is 4 ft. by 8 ft.
   How many sq. ft. is it?

   _____

9. How many sq. yds. are in a plot of land 40 yds. by 30 yds.?

   _____

10. How many sq. ft. are in a floor 4 yds. by 10 ft.?
    (Change yds. to ft., then multiply.)

    _____

11. How many sq. yds. are in an area 5 yds. by 9 ft.? (This time, change ft. to yds.)

    _____

12. How many sq. ft. are in an area 2 yds. by 11 ft.?

    _____

13. The floor finish you bought will cover 200 sq. ft.

    Will it cover a floor 15 ft. by 10 ft.?

    ☐ yes   ☐ no

14. 16 ounces = —————— (how many?) lbs.

15. 4 lbs. = —————— (how many?) oz.

16. Can A   Can B

$5\frac{1}{2}$ oz. $\frac{1}{2}$ lb.

Which is larger?

☐ Can A   ☐ Can B

17. How many ounces are in a package that weighs $2\frac{1}{4}$ lbs.? —————————————

18. 8 fluid ounces = —————— cup(s)

2 cups = —————— pint(s)

2 pints = —————— quart(s)

4 quarts = —————— gallon(s)

19. 1 quart =

☐ 8 fl. oz.   ☐ 16 fl. oz.   ☐ 32 fl. oz.

20. Which is bigger?

☐ 3 pints   ☐ 1 quart

21. Which is bigger?

☐ 3 quarts   ☐ 1 gallon

22. 3 gallons = —————— (how many?) quarts

23. Put these in order, smallest to largest:
centimeter   kilometer   millimeter   meter

————————————— smallest

————————————— next

————————————— next to largest

————————————— largest

24. 100 cm = —————— (how many?) meter(s)

25. 1 meter = a little more than —————— (how many?) yard(s)

26. 1 km =

☐ less than 1 mile   ☐ more than 1 mile

27. 6 feet = —————— (about how many?) meter(s)

28. Match:

80 km   about 39 in.

100 cm   about 50 miles

100 m   about 100 yds.

29. 1 liter is about equal to:

☐ 1 quart   ☐ 1 gallon

30. 1 gallon = ——————(about how many?) liter(s)

31. Which is bigger?

☐ 1 liter   ☐ 1 quart

32. Which is bigger?

☐ 1 kilogram   ☐ 1 pound

33. Which is bigger?

☐ 2 gallons   ☐ 4 liters

34. Fill in the numbers "1" and "2.2":

—————— kilogram = —————— pounds

35. Which is bigger?

☐ 5 kilograms   ☐ 7 pounds

Unit VIII.
MISCELLANEOUS LIFE SKILLS MATH

---

60. Seconds, Minutes, Hours, and Days

61. Telling Time

62. Hours Worked

63. A Person's Age

64. Graphs

65. Tables

66. Freezing, Boiling, and Normal Body Temperature

67. Review of Miscellaneous Life Skills Math Problems

60. Seconds, Minutes, Hours, and Days

QUICK REMINDER

60 seconds = 1 minute
60 minutes = 1 hour
24 hours = 1 day

EXERCISES

1. 5 minutes = —— (how many?) seconds

2. 5 hours = —— (how many?) minutes

3. 12 hours = —— (fraction) day

4. 30 minutes = —— (fraction) hour

5. 48 hours = —— (how many?) days

6. 180 seconds = —— (how many?) minutes

7. 120 minutes = —— (how many?) hours

8. Change 90 minutes into hours <u>and</u> minutes.

   —— hour(s) + —— minute(s)

9. Lois ran in a $\frac{1}{2}$ mile race. She finished in 130 seconds.
   Change her time into minutes and seconds.

   —— minute(s) + —— second(s)

10. You plan to cook a turkey for 240 minutes. How many hours must it cook?

    _____

61. Telling Time

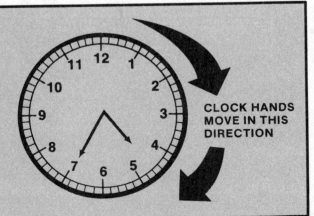

QUICK REMINDER

The little hand tells the <u>hour</u>:
Read the last number the little hand has passed.

The big hand tells how many <u>minutes</u> after the hour:
Start at the hour and count the marks.

<u>Or</u> figure there are 5 marks for each number. So multiply the number × 5 and add the extra marks.

CLOCK HANDS MOVE IN THIS DIRECTION

1. What time is it?

_____

2. What time is it?

_____

3. What time is it?

_____

4. What time is it?

_____

5. What time is it?

_____

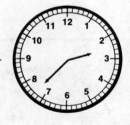

6. 4:50 means 50 minutes after 4.
4:50 is the same as 10 minutes to 5:00.

4:55 is the same as ——— minutes to 5:00

7. 10 minutes to 3:00 is the same as ———

minutes after 2.

8. What time is it?

_____

9. What time is it?

_____

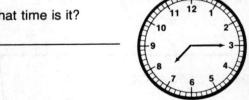

10. What time is it?

_____

62. Hours Worked

If you go to work in the morning and leave in the afternoon, how many hours have you worked?

First subtract the time you come to work from 12:00 (noon) to get morning hours worked.

But you can only subtract an even hour from 12:00. If you came after the hour, rewrite 12:00 as 11:60. Then you can subtract.

Next add the afternoon hours to the morning hours.

EXERCISES

1. You went to work at 9:00 in the morning and worked until 12:00 noon.

   How many hours did you work?

   _____

2. You went to work at 8:00 in the morning and worked until noon.

   How many hours did you work?

   _____

3. You went to work at 8:00 and worked until 1:00 in the afternoon.

   How many hours did you work?

   _____

4. You went to work at 8:00 in the morning and worked until 4:00 in the afternoon.

   How many hours did you work?

   _____

5. You went to work at 8:00 in the morning and worked until 4:00 in the afternoon. However, you took an hour for lunch. Many companies don't pay for lunch time.

   How many hours did you work?
   (Subtract out the hour for lunch.)

   _____

6. You went to work at 10:00 in the morning and worked until 2:30 in the afternoon.

   How many hours did you work? (Remember: 30 minutes is $\frac{1}{2}$ hour. Be sure to include this in your answer.)

   _____

7. You went to work at 10:00 and worked until 12:30 in the afternoon.

   How many hours did you work?

   _____

8. You went to work at 11:30 but only worked until 12:00.

   How long did you work? _____ (fraction) hour

9. You came to work at 9:30 and worked until noon.

   How many hours did you work?

   _____

10. You came to work at 8:30 and worked until 5:00. But you had a half hour for lunch.

    How many hours did you work?
    (Subtract out the half hour for lunch.)

    _____

63. A Person's Age

EXERCISES

1. How many months are there from October 1 to December 1?

   _____

2. How many months are there from October 1 to January 1 of the next year?

   _____

3. How many months are there from October 1 to March 1 of the next year?

   _____

4. How many months are there from October 1 to June 1 of the next year?

   _____

5. How many months are there from October 1 to October 1 of the next year?

   _____

6. Emile was born on August 4, 1968.
   How old was he on August 4, 1970?

   ——— years

7. Emile was born on August 4, 1968.
   How old was he on November 2, 1970? (Answer in years and months, rounded to the nearest month.)

   ——— years   ——— months

8. Emile was born on August 4, 1968.
   How old was he on December 5, 1970? (Again, round to the nearest month.)

   ——— years   ——— months

9. How old was Emile on January 4, 1971?

   ——— years   ——— months

10. How old was Emile on March 3, 1980?

   ——— years   ——— months

64. Graphs

EXERCISES

Look at this graph carefully. Then answer the following questions.

1. According to the graph, which went up more? Check it.

   ☐ big city spending
   ☐ cost of heavy fuel oil

2. Which prices rose more?

   ☐ movies
   ☐ newspaper

3. What does this graph tell you?

   ☐ A newspaper costs more than a cup of coffee.
   ☐ The price for a newspaper jumped more than the price of a movie over the past 30 years.

100%	200	300	400	500	600	700	800	900	1,000	1,100	1,200

HEAVY FUEL OIL
BIG CITY SPENDING
NEWSPAPER
HOME HEATING OIL
COFFEE
MOVIES
GASOLINE
MILK

RISING PRICES
1950-1980
(in percents)

4. Which of these prices rose the most?

   ☐ gasoline
   ☐ heavy fuel oil
   ☐ home heating oil

5. Which prices rose the least?

   ☐ big city budget   ☐ gasoline   ☐ milk

6. Which price rose about 300 percent?

   ☐ coffee   ☐ gasoline   ☐ newspaper

7. Which price rose between 400 and 500 percent?

   ☐ coffee   ☐ home heating oil   ☐ movies

8. Which prices increased more than 700%?

   ☐ milk   ☐ movies   ☐ newspaper

9. How much did big city spending increase?

   ☐ about 730%
   ☐ about 970%
   ☐ more than 1000%

10. How much did home heating oil costs go up?

    ☐ more than heavy fuel oil costs
    ☐ less than gasoline costs
    ☐ about 575%

Now look at the following graph. Then answer Questions 11-20.

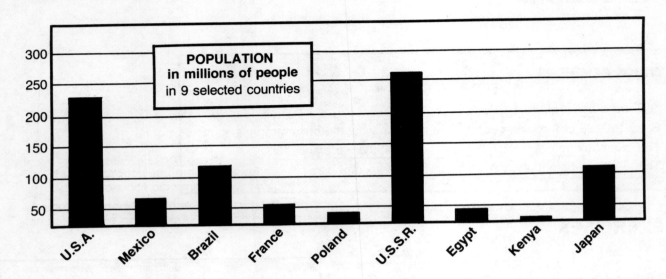

11. According to the graph, which country has more people?

☐ Egypt ☐ Mexico

12. Which country has more people?

☐ Brazil ☐ U.S.A.

13. Which of these three countries has the most people?

☐ Egypt ☐ France ☐ Mexico

14. Which of these three countries has the smallest population?

☐ Japan ☐ Mexico ☐ Poland

15. Which of the 9 countries on the graph has the largest population? _____

16. Which of the 9 countries on the graph has the smallest population? _____

17. The population of the U.S.A. is approximately

☐ 200 million ☐ 225 million ☐ 250 million

18. The population of the U.S.S.R. is

☐ 250 million ☐ 266 million ☐ 298 million

19. Which two countries are closest to each other in population?

☐ France and Kenya
☐ Japan and Brazil
☐ U.S.A. and Poland

20. The next-to-largest population shown on the graph belongs to _____.

106

65. Tables

EXERCISES

NORTHBOUND—Mon. thru Fri. except Hols.						
TO GRAND JUNCTION	AM	AM	AM	AM	PM	PM
Lv. Dolores	5:30	6:15	8:00	11:20	4:00	11:15
" La Plata	5:40	6:25	8:10	11:30	4:10	11:25
" Hermansville	5:50	6:35	8:20	11:40	4:20	11:35
" Top City	6:00	6:45	8:30	11:50	4:30	11:45
" Garamosa	6:10	6:55	8:40	12:00	4:40	11:55
" Roll Creek	6:20	7:05	8:50	12:10	4:50	12:05
" Hartsdale	6:30	7:15	9:00	12:20	5:00	12:15
" Iona	6:40	7:25	9:10	12:30	5:10	12:25
Arr. Grand Junction	6:50	7:35	9:20	12:40	5:20	12:35
	AM	AM	AM	PM	PM	AM

Look at this timetable carefully. Then answer the following questions.

1. When should you use this timetable?

☐ going from Dolores to Grand Junction only
☐ going from Grand Junction to Dolores only
☐ going either way

2. You want to travel from La Plata to Roll Creek on Saturday, Dec. 24. Can you use this timetable?

☐ yes   ☐ no

107

TO GRAND JUNCTION	AM	AM	AM	AM	PM	PM
Lv. Dolores	5:30	6:15	8:00	11:20	4:00	11:15
" La Plata	5:40	6:25	8:10	11:30	4:10	11:25
" Hermansville	5:50	6:35	8:20	11:40	4:20	11:35
" Top City	6:00	6:45	8:30	11:50	4:30	11:45
" Garamosa	6:10	6:55	8:40	12:00	4:40	11:55
" Roll Creek	6:20	7:05	8:50	12:10	4:50	12:05
" Hartsdale	6:30	7:15	9:00	12:20	5:00	12:15
" Iona	6:40	7:25	9:10	12:30	5:10	12:25
Arr. Grand Junction	6:50	7:35	9:20	12:40	5:20	12:35
	AM	AM	AM	PM	PM	AM

NORTHBOUND—Mon. thru Fri. except Hols.

Use this copy of the timetable for your answers.

3. You want to take the 5:30 AM train from Dolores. What time does this train arrive at Grand Junction? ——————————————

4. You want to take the 8:00 AM train from Dolores to Garamosa. You will arrive at Garamosa about
   ☐ 8:20 AM   ☐ 8:40 PM   ☐ 9:00 AM

5. You want to leave Top City and get into Grand Junction at 12:35 AM. The train you want leaves Top City at
   ☐ 11:15 PM   ☐ 11:45 PM   ☐ 11:45 AM

6. You want to leave Hermansville and get into Garamosa at noon. The best train for you leaves at
   ☐ 11:20 AM   ☐ 11:40 AM   ☐ 11:40 PM

7. The latest train you can take from Dolores that still gets you into Grand Junction in the morning is the
   ☐ 6:15 AM   ☐ 8:00 AM   ☐ 11:20 AM

8. The last train from La Plata at night leaves at
   ☐ 8:10   ☐ 11:30   ☐ 11:25

9. You are traveling from Top City to Iona. What direction are you going? ——————————————

10. You live in Hartsdale. Your job in Grand Junction starts at 8:00 AM. It takes you 15 minutes to get from the train station to your job. Which train will you take?
    ☐ The 6:15   ☐ The 7:15   ☐ The 8:00

Selected State Parks and Facilities	SIZE (IN ACRES)	CAMPING	CABINS	HOTEL	PICNICKING	HIKING	BOATING	FISHING	RIDING	SWIMMING	WINTER SPORTS
Asqually	24,000	●					●	●			
Bixby	210,018	●			●	●	●	●		●	●
Cullen Hills	5004	●	●		●	●			●		●
Dingle Bay	868			●	●		●	●		●	
Fasco	4280			●					●		
Lake Newall	360				●		●	●		●	
Mount Ness	691	●			●	●	●		●		●
Ridgely	1273	●		●				●			
Senoba	1300	●			●		●	●		●	

11. You are going to Asqually State Park. Which should you plan on doing?

☐ fishing   ☐ hiking   ☐ riding

12. You want to stay in a cabin in a state park. Which park is best for you?

☐ Cullen Hills   ☐ Fasco   ☐ Ridgely

13. You like riding, and you want to stay in a hotel. Your best bet is

☐ Cullen Hills   ☐ Fasco   ☐ Ridgely

14. You like camping in a place with lots and lots of acreage. Your best bet is

☐ Bixby   ☐ Lake Newall   ☐ Ridgely

15. You want to picnic and swim. The place for you is

☐ Cullen Hills   ☐ Mount Ness   ☐ Senoba

16. You like skiing. You'll probably find it at

☐ Bixby   ☐ Dingle Bay   ☐ Fasco

17. You want to spend a weekend in Senoba. You'll probably sleep in

☐ a tent or a camper   ☐ a cabin   ☐ a hotel

18. Which is the largest of these 3 state parks?

☐ Cullen Hills   ☐ Mount Ness   ☐ Senoba

19. You want to stay at a ski hotel. It looks like there's one at

☐ Fasco   ☐ Mt. Ness   ☐ Ridgely

20. You'd like a weekend boating and sleeping in a tent in the woods—maybe doing some fishing. You should check out

☐ Bixby   ☐ Fasco   ☐ Lake Newall

109

66. Freezing, Boiling, and Normal Body Temperature

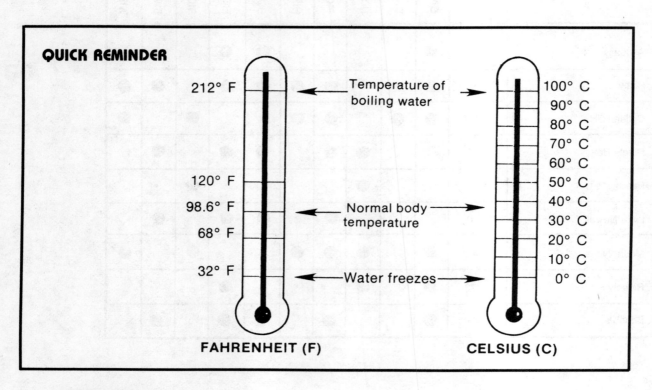

QUICK REMINDER

212° F ← Temperature of boiling water → 100° C

90° C
80° C
70° C
60° C

120° F

98.6° F ← Normal body temperature → 50° C

40° C

68° F

30° C
20° C
10° C

32° F ← Water freezes → 0° C

FAHRENHEIT (F)   **CELSIUS (C)**

EXERCISES

1. Which is the higher temperature?
   ☐ 100° Celsius (C)   ☐ 100° Fahrenheit (F)

2. Which is the higher temperature?
   ☐ 100° C   ☐ 120° F

3. Which is the higher temperature?
   ☐ 100° C   ☐ 200° F

4. Which is the colder temperature?
   ☐ 0° C   ☐ 0° F
   (Careful on this one: 0° F is way below the freezing point of 32° F.)

5. It is 10° F outside.
   Will water freeze?
   ☐ yes   ☐ no

6. It is 10° C outside.
   Will water freeze?
   ☐ yes   ☐ no

7. Cynthia's temperature is 101° F.
   This is:
   ☐ below normal   ☐ above normal

8. Water boils at 212°—
   ☐ Celsius   ☐ Fahrenheit

9. The temperature outside was 40° C. It was—
   ☐ cold   ☐ hot

10. Match: 5° C   water freezes

              32° F   just above freezing

              98.6° F   normal body temperature

              100° C   water boils

67. Review of Miscellaneous Life Skills Math Problems

EXERCISES

1. 1 minute = —————— (how many?) seconds

   1 hour = —————— (how many?) minutes

2. How many hours are there in a day?

   _____

3. How many seconds are in $1\frac{1}{2}$ minutes?

   _____

4. How many days are in 48 hours?

   _____

5. Change 205 minutes into hours and minutes.

   —————— hour(s) + —————— minute(s)

6. What time is it?

   _____

7. What time is it?

   _____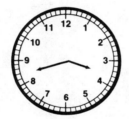

8.

   8:55 is the same as —————— minutes to 9:00.

9. You went to work at 9:30 in the morning and worked until 5:30 in the afternoon. But you had an hour off for lunch.

   How many hours did you work? (Subtract out the lunch time.)

   _____

111

10. You went to work at 9:30 in the morning and worked until 11:30 in the morning.

    How many hours did you work?

    _____

11. You went to work at 9:30 in the morning and worked until 12:30 in the afternoon.

    How many hours did you work?

    _____

12. How many months are there from September 20 to December 20?

    _____

13. How many months from September 20 to January 20 of the next year?

    _____

14. Rebecca was born on September 20, 1966.

    How old was she on January 18, 1980? (To nearest month.)

    ——— years ——— months

15. Mel was born on November 9, 1972.

    How old was he on February 12, 1982?

    ——— years ——— months

16. Match:

    0° C   32° F

    100° C   212° F

17. 30° F is—

    ☐ below freezing   ☐ above freezing

18. 30° C is—

    ☐ below freezing   ☐ above freezing

19. 110° F is—

    ☐ below the temperature of boiling water
    ☐ above the temperature of boiling water

20. Juanita's temperature was 98.6° F.

    This was—

    ☐ below normal   ☐ normal   ☐ above normal

Mi Primera Comunión

Ponga mi retrato aquí.

_____

(nombre)

_____

(fecha)

en

_____

(nombre de la iglesia)

La Eucaristía

Consultora principal del programa
Dra. Jane Marie Osterholt, SP

BROWN-ROA

A Division of Harcourt Brace & Company

Nihil obstat
Revdo. Richard L. Schaefer

Imprimátur
✠ Rvdo. Mayor Jerome Hanus OSB
Arzobispo de Dubuque
21 de agosto de 1998
Fiesta del Papa San Pío X
Patrono de los primeros comulgantes

El comité ad hoc encargado de vigilar el uso del Catecismo, National Conference of Catholic Bishops, determinó que esta serie catequista sigue el *Catecismo de la Iglesia Católica.*

La nihil obstat y el imprimátur son declaraciones oficiales de que un libro o folleto no tiene error doctrinal o moral. Lo presente no implica que aquéllos a quienes se les otorgó la nihil obstat y el imprimátur están de acuerdo con el contenido, las opiniones o las declaraciones expresados.

BROWN-ROA
A Division of Harcourt Brace & Company

Nuestra misión

La misión principal de BROWN-ROA es proveer a los mercados católicos los recursos catequistas impresos y audiovisuales de mayor calidad. El contenido de estos recursos reflejan los detalles más importantes de la investigación actual teológica, metodológica y pedagógica. Estos recursos son prácticos y fáciles de usar. Están diseñados para satisfacer necesidades de mercado específicas y están escritos para reflejar las enseñanzas de la Iglesia Católica.

Photography Credits
Cover: Stained-glass windows at Zimmerman Chapel, United Theological Seminary, Dayton, Ohio. Photography by Andy Snow Photographics.
Art Resource: National Museum of American Art: 73(c); **Gene Plaisted/The Crosiers:** 74; **Digital Imaging Group:** 10, 18, 23, 26, 27, 34, 42, 50, 51, 54, 63, 66, 67, 76, 77, 78, 79, 80; **FPG International:** Kevin Laubacher: 14; Arthur Tilley: 30; Dick Luria: 46; **John Barr/Gamma Liaison International:** 58; **Jack Holtel:** 7; **PhotoEdit:** David Young-Wolff: 38; Tony Freeman: 62; **Andy Snow Photographics:** 11, 19, 31, 35, 39, 55, 59, 75; **Superstock:** 72, 73(bl); **Tony Stone Images:** Daniel Bosler: 6; Bruce Ayres: 22; **Jim Whitmer:** 47. Special thanks to the parish communities at St. Charles Borromeo, Kettering; St. Paul's, Oakwood; and Holy Angels, Dayton, for cooperation with photography.

Illustration Credits
Biblical Art: Chris Vallo/The Mazer Corporation: 8–9, 16–17, 24–25, 32–33, 40–41, 48–49, 56–57, 64–65; **Children's Art:** 12–13, 20–21, 28–29, 36–37, 44–45, 52–53, 60–61, 68–69 (prepared by Chelsea Arney, Lisol Arney, Kaley Bartosik, Hannah Berry, Noah Berry, Morgan Brickley, Brittany King, Cecily King, Jackie Malone, Katie Malone, Bob Ninneman, Claudia Ninneman, Erica Ninneman, Laura Grace Ninneman, Brittany Smith, Lauren Vallo, Ryan Vallo, and the art classes of Holy Angels School, Dayton)

Printed in the United States of America

ISBN 0-15-950460-0

10 9 8 7 6 5 4

La Eucaristía

Mi Primera Comunión **4**

Una bendición de iniciación **5**

Capítulo 1
Pertenecer **6**

Capítulo 2
Invitados a la mesa **14**

Capítulo 3
Reunirse para celebrar **22**

Capítulo 4
Deleitarse con la palabra de Dios **30**

Capítulo 5
Ofrecer nuestros dones **38**

Capítulo 6
Recordar y dar gracias **46**

Capítulo 7
Compartir el pan de vida **54**

Capítulo 8
Ir a amar y a servir. **62**

Oraciones católicas **70**

La vida de Jesús **72**

La sagrada Comunión **74**

Glosario ilustrado de la misa **76**

Mi Primera Comunión

**Recibiré la
sagrada Comunión
por primera vez
durante la celebración de la Eucaristía
el**

_____

(fecha)

en

_____ .

(nombre de la iglesia)

**Le pido a mi familia, mis padrinos,
mi maestro, mis compañeros de clase, mis amigos
y toda la comunidad parroquial
que me ayuden a prepararme para esta celebración.**

_____

(firma)

**Éstas son las firmas de las personas que me ayudan
a prepararme para mi Primera Comunión.**

Una bendición de iniciación

"¡Soy el pan que da vida!
El que viene a mí no tendrá hambre jamás."

—Evangelio de San Juan 6, 35

Líder: Hoy nos reunimos para continuar la jornada de
iniciación
para prepararse para la Primera Comunión.
Estamos listos para aprender de los demás
y de nuestra comunidad de la Iglesia.
Y por eso rezamos:
Dios, nuestro Padre, acepta nuestras gracias y
elogios por tu gran amor.
Jesús, Hijo de Dios, que estés presente en el
sacramento de la Eucaristía.
Espíritu Santo, ayúdanos a crecer como miembros
del Cuerpo de Cristo.

Lector: Escuchemos el mensaje que Dios nos da:
(Lectura del Evangelio de San Juan 6, 32–40.)
Palabra de Dios.

Todos: **Demos gracias a Dios.**

Líder: Pidamos a Dios que nos bendiga en nuestra jornada.

Todos: **Santísima Trinidad, dirígenos a la mesa de la Eucaristía.**
Enséñanos a amarnos entre sí, así como Tú nos amas
a nosotros.
Ayúdanos a ser señales vivas de tu presencia
entre nosotros
y dirígenos a la plenitud de tu reino.
Oramos con las palabras que Jesús nos enseño.
(Se reza el Padrenuestro.)

Líder: Que el Señor esté con nosotros, ahora y siempre.

Todos: **¡Amén!**

Chapter 1
Belonging

Dear God—Father, Son, and Holy Spirit—you call us to new life. Help us grow as members of the Church. Amen!

Everyone needs to belong. When you belong, you share time and love with others. You help people, and they help you.

When did you become a member of your family?

Pertenecer

Amado Dios —Padre, Hijo y Espíritu Santo— nos llamas a una nueva vida. Ayúdanos a crecer como miembros de la Iglesia. ¡Amén!

Todos necesitamos sentir que pertenecemos. Es decir, compartir momentos y amor con los demás. Ayudas a la gente y la gente te ayuda a ti.

¿Cuándo te hiciste miembro de tu familia?

6 : Somos invitados

Tú también perteneces a la Iglesia Católica. Te hiciste miembro de la Iglesia cuando te bautizaron.

Ser miembro de la Iglesia significa que perteneces a Dios para siempre. Cuando te bautizaron, te convertiste en seguidor de Jesucristo. Te hiciste **cristiano**.

You belong to the Catholic Church, too. You became a member of the Church when you were baptized.

Belonging to the Church means belonging to God, forever. When you were baptized, you became a follower of Jesus Christ. You became a **Christian**.

Somos invitados : 7

In the Name of Jesus Christ

I remember that morning. I was in Jerusalem with my family for the Jewish feast of **Pentecost**. We saw a great crowd gathered. A man named Peter was speaking.

"Friends!" Peter said in a loud voice. You know that Jesus was a great teacher sent by God. Jesus died on a cross, but that was not the end of the story!"

En nombre de Jesucristo

Recuerdo esa mañana. Estaba en Jerusalén con mi familia celebrando la fiesta judía de **Pentecostés**. Vimos a una gran muchedumbre. Un hombre llamado Pedro hablaba.

—¡Amigos! —dijo Pedro en voz alta—. Saben que Jesucristo fue el gran maestro enviado por Dios. Jesús murió en la cruz, pero la historia no terminó allí.

"God set Jesus free from death," Peter continued. "Jesus rose from the tomb, and now he is with his Father in heaven. This very day he sent the **Holy Spirit** to us as he had promised. That promise is not just for us, his friends. It is for you and your children, too!"

"What must we do?" my father called out.

"Turn to God, my friend," Peter answered. "Be baptized in the name of Jesus Christ. Then you will receive God's Holy Spirit, too."

That morning I was baptized with my whole family. Now we all belong to the family of Jesus Christ.

—based on Acts 2

—Dios liberó a Jesús de la muerte —continuó Pedro—. Jesús resucitó de la tumba y ahora está con su Padre en el cielo. Este mismo día nos envió al **Espíritu Santo** como lo había prometido. No sólo por nosotros, sus amigos, sino también por ustedes y sus hijos.

—¿Qué debemos hacer? —enunció mi padre.

—Unirse a Dios, mi amigo —contestó Pedro—. Ser bautizado en nombre de Cristo. Entonces, también recibirás al Espíritu Santo.

Esa mañana me bautizaron con toda mi familia. Ahora todos pertenecemos a la familia de Jesucristo.

—basado en los Hechos de los apóstoles 2

Baptism and Confirmation

The Catholic Church welcomes new members through Baptism, Confirmation, and Eucharist. These sacraments are called **Sacraments of Initiation**, or "belonging."

We celebrate Baptism with water and holy words. All living things need water to stay alive. We need the water of Baptism to have new life forever with God.

The words of Baptism tell us that we belong to God. "I baptize you in the name of the Father, and of the Son, and of the Holy Spirit."

El Bautismo y la Confirmación

La Iglesia Católica recibe a nuevos miembros por medio del Bautismo, la Confirmación y la Eucaristía. Estos sacramentos se llaman los **sacramentos de iniciación**.

Celebramos el Bautismo con agua y palabras santas. Todos los seres vivos necesitan agua para vivir. Nosotros necesitamos el agua del Bautismo para vivir eternamente en Dios.

Las palabras del Bautismo nos dicen que pertenecemos a Dios. "Te bautizo en el nombre del Padre, del Hijo y del Espíritu Santo."

Celebramos la Confirmación con la **unción** de aceite bendito y la imposición de manos. Se usa aceite para fortalecer el cuerpo. La Confirmación nos ayuda a aumentar nuestra fe. Le tendemos la mano a los que necesitan el amor de Dios.

Las palabras de Confirmación nos dicen que se nos ha concedido el Espíritu Santo de una manera especial. "Reciban el sello del Espíritu Santo."

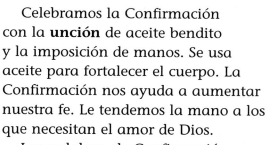

Preguntamos

¿Por qué el Bautismo es el primer sacramento?

El Bautismo nos hace miembros de la Iglesia y nos une a Jesucristo. En el Bautismo compartimos primero el **misterio pascual** de la muerte de Cristo y **la resurrección**. Los demás sacramentos se basan en la gracia del Bautismo.
(Catecismo, #1213–1214)

We celebrate Confirmation by being **anointed** with holy oil and by the laying on of hands. Oil is used to make the body strong. Confirmation helps us grow strong in our faith. We reach out to others who need God's love.

The words of Confirmation tell us that we have been given the Holy Spirit in a special way. "Be sealed with the Gift of the Holy Spirit."

We Ask

Why is Baptism the first sacrament?

Baptism makes us members of the Church and joins us to Jesus. In Baptism we first share in the **Paschal mystery** of Jesus' death and **resurrection**. All the other sacraments build on the grace of Baptism.
(Catechism, #1213–1214)

I Am Signed with the Cross

On the cross, write or draw one way you can show that you belong to Jesus Christ and the Church.

La Señal de la Cruz

En la cruz, escribe o dibuja una manera en que puedas mostrar que perteneces a Jesucristo y a la Iglesia.

12 : Vivimos la Eucaristía

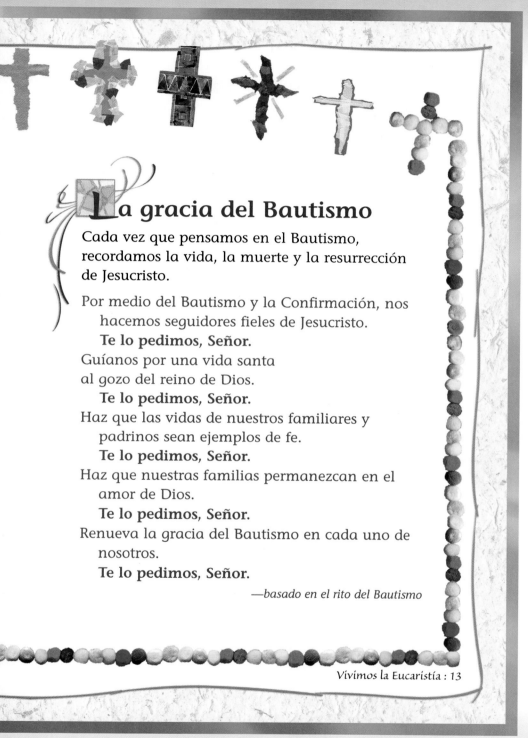

La gracia del Bautismo

Cada vez que pensamos en el Bautismo, recordamos la vida, la muerte y la resurrección de Jesucristo.

Por medio del Bautismo y la Confirmación, nos hacemos seguidores fieles de Jesucristo.
Te lo pedimos, Señor.
Guíanos por una vida santa
al gozo del reino de Dios.
Te lo pedimos, Señor.
Haz que las vidas de nuestros familiares y padrinos sean ejemplos de fe.
Te lo pedimos, Señor.
Haz que nuestras familias permanezcan en el amor de Dios.
Te lo pedimos, Señor.
Renueva la gracia del Bautismo en cada uno de nosotros.
Te lo pedimos, Señor.

—basado en el rito del Bautismo

Vivimos la Eucaristía : 13

The Grace of Baptism

Every time we recall our Baptism, we remember Jesus' life, death, and resurrection.

Through Baptism and Confirmation,
make us faithful followers of Jesus Christ.
Lord, hear our prayer.
Lead us by a holy life
to the joys of God's kingdom.
Lord, hear our prayer.
Make the lives of our families and godparents
signs of faith for us to follow.
Lord, hear our prayer.
Keep our families always in God's love.
Lord, hear our prayer.
Renew the grace of Baptism in each of us.
Lord, hear our prayer.

—based on the Rite of Baptism

Chapter 2
Invited to the Table

Dear God—Father, Son, and Holy Spirit—you have called us to the table of the Eucharist. Help us live as members of the Body of Christ. Amen!

What if you went to a family party and there was no place for you at the dinner table? You would probably feel left out. Sharing a meal is a big part of any celebration. When you are invited to sit at the table, you really feel that you belong.

What do you like best about sharing meals?

Capítulo 2
Invitados a la mesa

Amado Dios —Padre, Hijo y Espíritu Santo— nos has llamado a la mesa de la Eucaristía. Ayúdanos a vivir como miembros del cuerpo de Cristo. ¡Amén!

¿Qué pasaría si fueras a una fiesta de la familia y no tuvieras un puesto en la mesa de la cena? Probablemente te sentirías excluido. La comida es una gran parte de cualquier celebración. Cuando te invitan a sentarte en la mesa, te sientes que realmente perteneces al grupo.

¿Qué es lo que más te gusta de compartir las comidas?

14 : Somos invitados

Our Catholic family shares a very special meal, the **Eucharist**. The Mass is our celebration of the Sacrament of the Eucharist. At Mass we receive Jesus himself in the form of the sacred Bread and Wine. The altar is our family table.

You have celebrated the Eucharist before by coming to Mass with your family and your class. But now you are getting ready to share completely in our holy meal. You are invited to come to the table and receive Jesus in **Holy Communion**.

Nuestra familia católica comparte una comida muy especial, la **Eucaristía**. La misa es la celebración del sacramento de la Eucaristía. En la misa recibimos a Jesucristo en la forma del pan y el vino sagrados. El altar es la mesa de la familia.

Has celebrado la Eucaristía antes de ir a misa con tu familia y tu clase. Pero ahora te preparas para compartir por completo la cena sagrada. Estás invitado a la mesa y a recibir a Jesús en la **sagrada Comunión**.

The Vine and the Branches

On the night before he died, Jesus went with his friends to a garden to pray. Jesus' friends were sad. They thought they would never see Jesus again. They wanted to stay close to him.

La vid y los sarmientos

En la noche antes de morir, Jesús fue con sus amigos al huerto a rezar. Los amigos de Jesús estaban tristes. Pensaban que nunca verían de nuevo a Jesús. Querían estar cerca de Él.

16 : Recordamos

Jesús quería hallar una manera de decirles a sus amigos que nunca se separarían de Él. Miró la bella vid que crecía en la pared del huerto. Ésta le dio una idea para su historia.

—Soy la vid —dijo Jesús—. Mi Padre en el cielo es el labrador. El labrador cuida la vid y sus sarmientos. Uds. son los sarmientos de la vid. Si permanecen en mí, los sarmientos seguirán creciendo.

—Uds. son mis amigos —dijo Jesús—, y yo los amo. Permanezcan en mi amor y todo lo que hagan reflejará el amor de Dios. Y serán como fuertes sarmientos de la vid que produce muchos frutos buenos.

—basado en el evangelio de San Juan 15, 1–17

Jesus wanted to find a way to tell his friends they would never be separated from him. He looked at a beautiful grapevine growing along the garden wall. The grapevine gave Jesus an idea for a story.

"I am the vine," Jesus said. "My Father in heaven is the gardener. The gardener takes care of the vine and its branches. You are the branches of the vine. As long as you stay close to me, the branches will keep growing.

"You are my friends," Jesus said, "and I love you. Keep living in my love. Then everything you do will show God's love. Then you will be like strong branches of the grapevine that bear lots of good fruit."

—based on John 15:1–17

First Communion

We want to be joined closely to Jesus like the branches of the grapevine. So we celebrate the Sacraments of Initiation. We are baptized. We are sealed with the Holy Spirit in Confirmation. We receive Jesus in Holy Communion for the first time.

La Primera Comunión

Queremos estar muy cerca de Jesús como los sarmientos de la vid. Por eso celebramos los sacramentos de iniciación. Somos bautizados. Recibimos el sello del Espíritu Santo en la Confirmación. Recibimos a Jesús en la sagrada Comunión por primera vez.

18 : Celebramos

Los sacramentos de iniciación nos unen a Jesús y a todos sus discípulos. Somos el **Cuerpo de Cristo**.

Personas de todas las edades celebran los sacramentos de iniciación para hacernos miembros totales de la Iglesia. Algunos católicos celebran los tres sacramentos al mismo tiempo. Otros católicos son bautizadoes de bebés. Entonces celebran la Primera Reconciliación y la Primera Comunión a los siete años aproximadamente. Son confirmados un poco después.

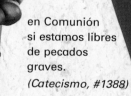

Preguntamos

¿Con qué frecuencia debemos recibir la Comunión?

El Bautismo y la Confirmación se reciben una vez en la vida. Nos marcan como discípulos de Dios para siempre. Pero al recibir la Primera Comunión, se espera que vayamos a la mesa del Señor una y otra vez en nuestras vidas. Cada vez que celebramos la Eucaristía en la misa, recibimos a Jesús en Comunión si estamos libres de pecados graves.
(Catecismo, #1388)

Celebramos : 19

The Sacraments of Initiation join us together with Jesus and with all his followers. We are the **Body of Christ**.

People of all ages celebrate the Sacraments of Initiation to become full members of the Church. Some Catholics celebrate all three sacraments at the same time. Other Catholics are baptized as babies. Then around the age of seven they celebrate First Reconciliation and First Communion. They are confirmed some time later.

We Ask

How often should we receive Communion?

Baptism and Confirmation are once-in-a-lifetime celebrations. They mark us as God's own forever. But once we have received First Communion, we are encouraged to come to the table again and again throughout our lives. Each time we celebrate the Eucharist at Mass, we should receive Jesus in Communion if we are free of serious sin.
(Catechism, #1388)

My Answer to Jesus

Jesus invites you to grow closer to him by receiving your First Communion. Finish the sentence in your own words. Sign your name.

**Dear Jesus,
Thank you for inviting me to the table of the Eucharist. I want to receive Communion because**

_____

_____

_____

_____

Love,

_____

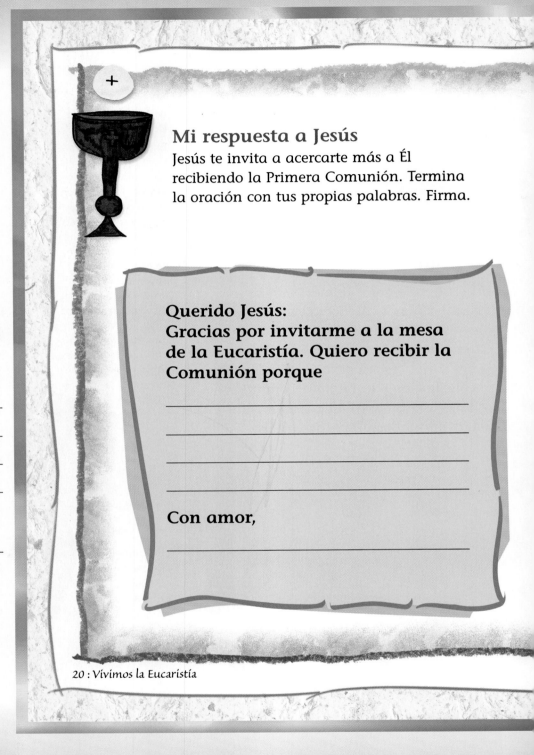

Mi respuesta a Jesús

Jesús te invita a acercarte más a Él recibiendo la Primera Comunión. Termina la oración con tus propias palabras. Firma.

**Querido Jesús:
Gracias por invitarme a la mesa de la Eucaristía. Quiero recibir la Comunión porque**

_____

_____

_____

_____

Con amor,

_____

Juntos en una mesa

Le agradecemos a Dios el don de la Eucaristía.

Dios nuestro Padre,
Jesús nos trajo las buenas noticias.
Nos mostró el camino del amor.
Nos une en una sola mesa
y nos pide que hagamos lo que Él hizo.
   ¡Gloria a Dios en el cielo!
Padre nuestro que estás en el cielo,
nos has llamado a recibir
el cuerpo y la sangre de Cristo en esta mesa
y a ser llenados con el gozo del Espíritu Santo.
Por medio de esta sagrada cena, danos la fuerza
para complacerte más y más.
   ¡Gloria a Dios en el cielo!

—basado en la Oración eucarística III para niños

Vivimos la Eucaristía : 21

Together to One Table

We thank God for the gift of the Eucharist.

God our Father,
Jesus brought us the
   good news.
He showed us the way
   of love.
He brings us together to
   one table
and asks us to do what
   he did.
   **Glory to God in the
   highest!**
Father in heaven,
you have called us to
   receive
the Body and Blood of
   Christ at this table
and be filled with the joy
   of the Holy Spirit.
Through this holy meal,
   give us the strength
to please you more
   and more.
   **Glory to God in the
   highest!**

—based on Eucharistic Prayer III
for Children

Chapter 3
Gathering to Celebrate

Dear God—Father, Son, and Holy Spirit—we come together as a family at Mass. Welcome us as we welcome one another. Amen!

It's no fun to celebrate alone. Good times are better when you share them with others. Family members, friends, and neighbors are part of your **community**, the group of people with whom you share special times.

What are some things you like to do when you get together with family members and friends?

Reunirse para celebrar

Amado Dios —Padre, Hijo y Espíritu Santo— nos reunimos como una familia en la misa. Recíbenos como recibimos a los demás. ¡Amén!

No es divertido celebrar uno solo. Los momentos buenos son mejores cuando se comparten con otros. Los familiares, amigos y vecinos son parte de tu **comunidad**, el grupo de personas con las que compartes momentos especiales.

¿Cuáles son algunas de las cosas que te gusta hacer cuando te reúnes con familiares y amigos?

También celebramos la Eucaristía con una comunidad. Para la misa nos reunimos con miembros de nuestra Iglesia, la **parroquia**.

Reunirnos para la misa es como reunirse para otras celebraciones. Recibimos a los demás, cantamos para compartir nuestra alegría y recordamos la misericordia y el perdón de Dios.

We celebrate the Eucharist with a community, too. We come together for Mass with members of our Church family, the **parish**.

Gathering for Mass is like gathering for other celebrations. We greet one another. We share our joy in singing. We remember God's mercy and forgiveness.

Like Family to One Another

The first Christians made the Eucharist the center of their lives. Every week they went to the Temple to pray, just as they always had. Then they gathered in one home or another to remember Jesus.

Before sharing the Lord's Body and Blood, the people remembered with joy their Baptism and the coming of the Holy Spirit. They sang songs of praise to God.

The Christians were like family to one another. Everyone was welcome. Everyone shared. Rich people shared what they had with those who were poor. People who had no money shared their prayers and their talents, helping one another.

Somos una familia

Los primeros cristianos hacían de la Eucaristía el centro de sus vidas. Cada semana iban a orar al templo como lo habían hecho siempre. Luego, se reunían en una casa para recordar a Jesús.

Antes de compartir el Cuerpo y la Sangre del Señor, las personas recordaban con alegría su bautismo y la llegada del Espíritu Santo. Cantaban canciones de alabanza a Dios.

Los cristianos eran como una familia. Todos compartían y eran bienvenidos. Los adinerados compartían lo que tenían con los pobres. Los que no tenían dinero compartían sus oraciones y talentos ayudando a los demás.

These first followers of Jesus amazed all who saw them. "Look!" the people said. "See how these Christians love one another!"

—based on Acts 2:42–47

Estos primeros seguidores de Jesús asombraban a todos los que los veían. —¡Miren! —decía la gente—. ¡Vean como estos cristianos se aman unos a otros!

—basado en los Hechos de los apóstoles 2, 42–47

Recordamos : 25

The Mass Begins

From the very beginning, it's easy to see that the Mass is a celebration. We begin with a song and a parade. The song is a **hymn**, or holy song. The parade is a **procession** of ministers who will help us celebrate.

The prayers and actions of the beginning of the Mass are called the **Introductory Rites**. They help us turn our hearts and minds to the great celebration of the Eucharist.

Comienza la misa

Desde el comienzo, es fácil ver que la misa es una celebración. Comenzamos con una canción y un desfile. La canción es un **himno** o canción sagrada. El desfile es una **procesión** de sacerdotes que nos ayudarán a celebrar.

Las oraciones y los actos del comienzo de la misa se llaman **ritos iniciales**. Nos ayudan a concentrar nuestros corazones y nuestras mentes en la gran celebración de la Eucaristía.

Jesús está realmente presente en cada parte de la misa. Él está verdaderamente con nosotros en la Comunión, pero también está con nosotros en el sacerdote que **preside** o dirige nuestra celebración. Está presente en los otros sacerdotes y en todos nosotros, la **congregación**.

En la misa nos reunimos para celebrar el mismo misterio pascual que celebramos en el Bautizo. Nos bendecimos con agua de la fuente bautismal o fuente de agua bendita cuando llegamos a la iglesia. La misa comienza con la Señal de la Cruz, las mismas palabras con las que nos bautizaron. "En el nombre del Padre, del Hijo y del Espíritu Santo. ¡Amén!"

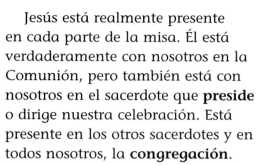

Preguntamos

¿Por qué celebramos la Eucaristía cada semana?

Reunirnos para la misa cada semana es mostrar que pertenecemos al Cuerpo de Cristo. Tenemos un **deber** de participar en la misa una vez a la semana, el domingo o el sábado en la tarde o los días de fiesta. Mientras más celebramos, más nos acercamos a Jesús y al prójimo. *(Catecismo #2180–2182)*

Jesus is really present in every part of the Mass. He is most truly with us in Communion, but he is also with us in the priest who **presides** over, or leads, our celebration. He is present in the other ministers. He is present in all of us, the **assembly**.

At Mass we gather to celebrate the same Paschal mystery we celebrate in Baptism. We bless ourselves with water from the baptismal font or holy water font when we come into the church. The Mass begins with the Sign of the Cross, the same words with which we were baptized. "In the name of the Father, and of the Son, and of the Holy Spirit. Amen!"

We Ask

Why do we celebrate the Eucharist every week?

Gathering for Mass every week is how we show that we belong to the Body of Christ. We have a **duty** to participate in the Mass once a week, on Sunday or on Saturday evening, and on holy days. The more we celebrate, the closer we come to Jesus and to one another. *(Catechism, #2180–2182)*

I Come to Celebrate

In the space below, draw or glue pictures of people who will gather at Mass to celebrate with you on the day you receive First Communion.

Voy a celebrar

En el siguiente espacio, haz o pega dibujos de personas que se reunirán en la misa para celebrar contigo el día que recibas la Primera Comunión.

28 : *Vivimos la Eucaristía*

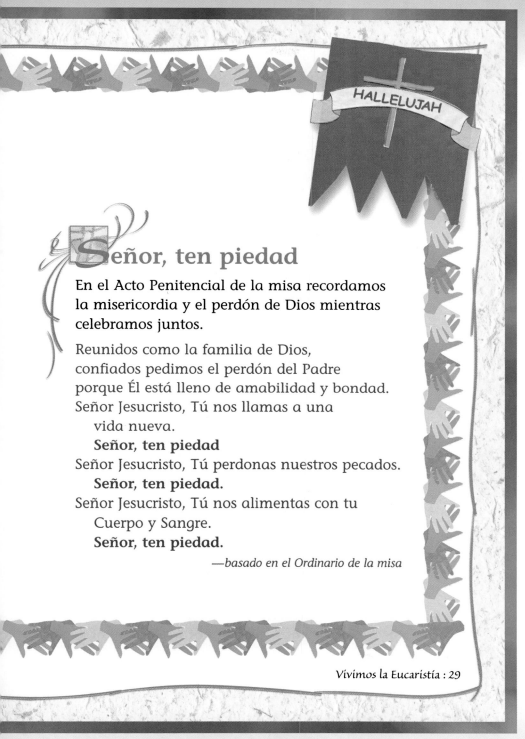

Señor, ten piedad

En el Acto Penitencial de la misa recordamos la misericordia y el perdón de Dios mientras celebramos juntos.

Reunidos como la familia de Dios,
confiados pedimos el perdón del Padre
porque Él está lleno de amabilidad y bondad.
Señor Jesucristo, Tú nos llamas a una
vida nueva.
Señor, ten piedad
Señor Jesucristo, Tú perdonas nuestros pecados.
Señor, ten piedad.
Señor Jesucristo, Tú nos alimentas con tu
Cuerpo y Sangre.
Señor, ten piedad.

—basado en el Ordinario de la misa

Lord, Have Mercy

In the Penitential Rite at Mass, we recall God's mercy and forgiveness as we celebrate together.

Coming together as God's
family,
with confidence let us ask
the Father's forgiveness,
for he is full of gentleness
and kindness.
Lord Jesus, you raise us to
new life.
Lord, have mercy.
Lord Jesus, you forgive us
our sins.
Lord, have mercy.
Lord Jesus, you feed us with
your Body and Blood.
Lord, have mercy.

—based on the Order of the Mass

Chapter 4
Feasting on God's Word

Dear God—Father, Son, and Holy Spirit—your word is good news to us. Help us hear your word and live by it. Amen!

Some stories are so good you want to hear them over and over. Good stories are like good news. They make you laugh or give you hope. A good story can be like a feast of good food, shared with people you love.

What is one of your favorite stories?

Capítulo 4
Deleitarse con la palabra de Dios

Amado Dios —Padre, Hijo y Espíritu Santo— tu palabra son buenas noticias para nosotros. Ayúdanos a oír tu palabra y vivirla. ¡Amén!

Algunas historias son tan buenas que quieres escucharlas una y otra vez. Las historias buenas son como las noticias buenas, te hacen reír o te dan esperanza. Una historia buena puede ser como un buen banquete de comida que compartes con personas que amas.

¿Cuál es una de tus historias favoritas?

30 : Somos invitados

Nuestra familia católica también comparte historias maravillosas. En la misa oímos las noticias buenas del amor de Dios en las palabras de las **Sagradas Escrituras**. Cuando escuchamos es como si Dios nos hablara directamente. La palabra de Dios es parte de la sagrada cena de la Eucaristía.

Our Catholic family shares wonderful stories, too. At Mass we hear the good news of God's love in the words of the **Scriptures**. When we listen, it is as though God is speaking right to us. The feast of God's word is part of the holy meal of the Eucharist.

Somos invitados : 31

Jesus, the Good Shepherd

Jesus knew that people needed to hear the good news of God's love. So one day Jesus compared himself to a shepherd, a person who cares for a flock of sheep. In Jesus' day almost everyone had seen shepherds at work in the fields.

"I am the good shepherd," Jesus told the people. "Just as a shepherd cares for all the sheep, so I care for you. I know you by name, just as a shepherd knows his sheep."

Jesus continued. "You have seen how a shepherd lies down in front of the sheep gate at night, to stay on guard. When the shepherd is there, the sheep are safe. Even if a wolf comes, the good shepherd will not run away. The good shepherd would rather die than see one of the sheep hurt. In the same way, I will give up my life so that you will be saved."

Jesús, el buen pastor

Jesús sabía que las personas necesitaban oír la buena noticia del amor de Dios. Así que un día, Jesús se comparó con un pastor, una persona que cuida de un rebaño de ovejas. En los tiempos de Jesús casi todos habían visto pastores trabajando en los campos.

—Soy el buen pastor —le dijo Jesús a la gente—. Así como el pastor cuida de todas las ovejas, yo cuido de ustedes. Los conozco por nombre así como el pastor conoce a sus ovejas.

Continuó Jesús: —Uds. han visto cómo un pastor se acuesta frente a la cerca de su rebaño en la noche para protegerlo. Cuando el pastor está allí, las ovejas están seguras. El buen pastor no huirá aunque llegue un lobo. El buen pastor preferiría morir antes de ver herida a una de sus ovejas. De la misma manera daría mi vida para salvarlos.

Not everyone in the crowd understood Jesus' story, but some people did. The people who listened and understood were happy. They knew God loved them very much.

—based on John 10:1–18

No todos en la multitud comprendían la historia de Jesús, pero otros sí. Las personas que escuchaban y comprendían eran felices. Sabían que Dios los quería mucho.

—basado en el evangelio de San Juan 10, 1–18

Sharing the Word

We share God's word in the part of the Mass called the **Liturgy of the Word**. At Sunday Mass we hear three readings from the Bible. Between the first two readings, we sing or pray a **psalm** as our response, or answer, to God's word.

The readings tell us the good news of God's love. In fact, the third reading is called the **gospel**, which means "good news." This reading is from the part of the Bible that tells about Jesus' life and teachings. We greet the gospel reading with a song or shout of joy, "**Alleluia!**"

Compartir la palabra

Compartimos la palabra de Dios en la parte de la misa llamada **Liturgia de la palabra**. En la misa dominical oímos tres lecturas de la Biblia. Entre las primeras dos lecturas cantamos o rezamos un **salmo** como respuesta a la palabra de Dios.

Las lecturas nos dicen la buena noticia del amor de Dios. De hecho, la tercera lectura se llama el **evangelio**, que significa "buenas noticias". Esta lectura es de la parte de la Biblia que nos habla de la vida y las enseñanzas de Jesús. Recibimos la lectura del evangelio con una canción o grito de alegría "**¡Aleluya!**"

Después de las lecturas, el sacerdote o diácono da una **homilía** para ayudarnos a comprender y seguir la palabra de Dios. Luego, nos paramos y orgullosos decimos lo que creemos rezando el **Credo**.

Terminamos la Liturgia de la palabra orando por las necesidades de todas las personas del mundo. Deleitarse con la palabra de Dios nos hace querer compartir con otros que están deseosos de buenas noticias.

Preguntamos

¿Cómo hallamos a Jesús en la palabra de Dios?

Creemos que las Sagradas Escrituras son las palabras propias de Dios escritas en palabras humanas. Las buenas noticias de la Biblia son las mismas que llevó Jesús. Un nombre para Jesús es "la palabra de Dios". Así que cuando compartimos la palabra de Dios en las Sagradas Escrituras, hallamos a Jesús, la palabra viviente de Dios.
(Catecismo, #101–104)

After the readings the priest or deacon gives a **homily** to help us understand and follow God's word. Then we stand and proudly tell what we believe by praying the **Creed**.

We close the Liturgy of the Word by praying together for the needs of all people around the world. Feasting on God's word makes us want to share with others who are hungry for good news.

We Ask

How do we meet Jesus in God's word?

We believe that the Scriptures are God's own word, written down in human words. The good news of the Bible is the same good news that Jesus brought. One name for Jesus is "the Word of God." So when we share the word of God in the Scriptures, we are meeting Jesus, God's living Word.
(Catechism, #101–104)

I Hear Good News

In the space below, draw or write about one of your favorite Bible stories.

Escucho la buena noticia

En el siguiente espacio, dibuja o escribe sobre una de tus historias preferidas de la Biblia.

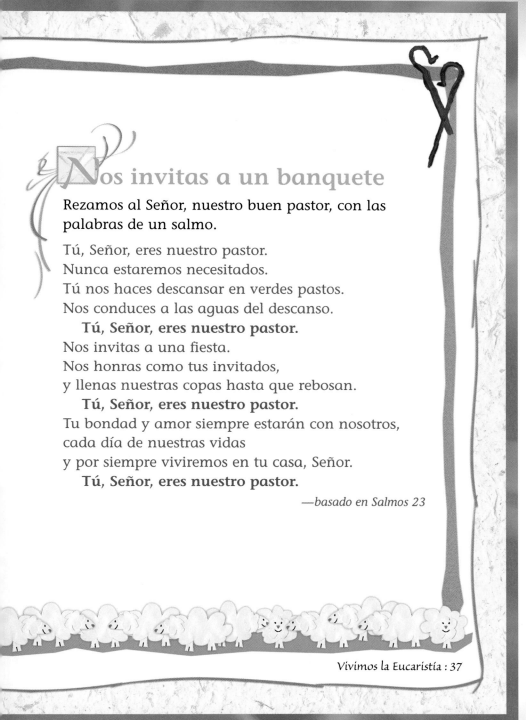

Nos invitas a un banquete

Rezamos al Señor, nuestro buen pastor, con las palabras de un salmo.

Tú, Señor, eres nuestro pastor.
Nunca estaremos necesitados.
Tú nos haces descansar en verdes pastos.
Nos conduces a las aguas del descanso.
   Tú, Señor, eres nuestro pastor.
Nos invitas a una fiesta.
Nos honras como tus invitados,
y llenas nuestras copas hasta que rebosan.
   Tú, Señor, eres nuestro pastor.
Tu bondad y amor siempre estarán con nosotros,
cada día de nuestras vidas
y por siempre viviremos en tu casa, Señor.
   Tú, Señor, eres nuestro pastor.

—*basado en Salmos 23*

You Treat Us to a Feast

We pray to the Lord, our good shepherd, in the words of a psalm.

You, Lord, are our
   shepherd.
We will never be in need.
You let us rest in fields of
   green grass.
You lead us to streams of
   peaceful water.
   **You, Lord, are our
   shepherd.**
You treat us to a feast.
You honor us as your
   guests,
and you fill our cup until
   it overflows.
   **You, Lord, are our
   shepherd.**
Your kindness and love will
   always be with us,
each day of our lives,
and we will live forever in
   your house, Lord.
   **You, Lord, are our
   shepherd.**

—*based on Psalm 23*

Chapter 5
Offering Our Gifts

Dear God—Father, Son, and Holy Spirit—you give us every good thing. Help us share our gifts with others. Amen!

When people gather for a special meal, they sometimes bring gifts of food.

What special foods does your family share? What kind of food would you bring to a special meal?

Capítulo 5
Ofrecer nuestros dones

Amado Dios —Padre, Hijo y Espíritu Santo— Tú nos das todas las cosas buenas. Ayúdanos a compartir nuestros dones con los demás. ¡Amén!

Algunas veces las personas llevan alimentos como regalo cuando se reúnen para una comida especial.

¿Qué alimentos especiales comparte tu familia? ¿Qué clase de alimento llevarías a una comida especial?

La misa es nuestra comida familiar católica. Llevamos para compartir los dones del pan y el vino, que se convierten en el Cuerpo y la Sangre de Jesús.

También compartimos otras cosas en la misa. Nos ofrecemos a Dios y a los demás. Ofrecemos los dones monetarios para ayudar con el trabajo de la parroquia y para los necesitados.

The Mass is our Catholic family meal. We bring gifts of bread and wine to share. The bread and wine become Jesus' own Body and Blood.

We share other things at Mass, too. We offer the gift of ourselves to God and to one another. We offer gifts of money to support the work of the parish and to help those who are in need.

The Wonderful Picnic

"Does anyone have any food to share?" I heard the man named Philip ask. Thousands of people were sitting on the grass listening to Jesus teach. All the people shook their heads. No one had thought to bring food.

I took a deep breath. "Sir!" I called out. I have five loaves of bread and a couple of fish."

The people around me laughed. Philip looked angry. "That's not enough food to feed even five people, never mind five thousand!" he said.

But I was looking at Jesus. He was smiling. He motioned for me to come forward. Jesus looked into my eyes and thanked me. He took the basket of food I held out to him.

El picnic maravilloso

—¿Alguien tiene alimentos para compartir? —oí preguntar a Felipe. Miles de personas estaban sentadas en la grama escuchando las enseñanzas de Jesús. Todos movieron sus cabezas. Nadie había pensado en llevar alimentos.

Respiré profundamente. —¡Señor! —exclamé—. Tengo cinco panes de centeno y un par de pescados.

La gente se rió a mi alrededor. Felipe parecía enojado. —Eso no basta para alimentar a cinco personas y menos a cinco mil —dijo él.

Pero observaba a Jesús. Él sonreía y me indicaba con un gesto que me acercara. Jesús me miró a los ojos y me agradeció. Él tomó la cesta con comida que le ofrecí.

Jesús tomó el pan en sus manos y lo bendijo. —Felipe —dijo Él—. Tú y los demás pasen este alimento a la gente. Asegúrense de que todos tengan suficiente para comer.

Algo maravilloso sucedió ese día. Más de cinco mil personas tuvieron el mejor picnic con mis cinco panes de centeno y dos pescados. Al terminar la comida, ¡sobraron doce cestas!

—Gracias por compartir —me dijo Jesús. Y Felipe hasta sonrió.

—*basado en el evangelio de San Juan 6, 5–13*

Jesus took the bread in his hands and prayed the meal blessing. "Philip," he said. "You and the others pass this food to the people. Make sure everyone has enough to eat."

Something wonderful happened that day. From my five loaves and two fish, more than five thousand people had the best picnic ever. When the meal was finished, there were twelve baskets of leftovers!

"Thank you for sharing," Jesus said to me. And even Philip smiled.

—*based on John 6:5–13*

Our Offering to God

The second part of the Mass, following the Liturgy of the Word, is called the **Liturgy of the Eucharist**. During this part of the Mass, we offer our gifts and prayers to God the Father. Our greatest offering is Jesus, who offers himself to the Father through the Holy Spirit. In the form of the sacred Bread and Wine, Jesus offers himself to us in Holy Communion.

Nuestras ofrendas a Dios

La segunda parte de la misa después de la Liturgia de la palabra se llama la **Liturgia de la Eucaristía**. Durante esta parte de la misa, ofrecemos nuestros dones y oraciones a Dios el Padre. Nuestra mayor ofrenda es Jesús, quien se ofrece al Padre por medio del Espíritu Santo. Jesús se nos ofrece en la sagrada Comunión, en la forma del pan y vino sagrados.

42 : Celebramos

En la **presentación de las ofrendas**, los miembros de la congregación llevan el pan y el vino al sacerdote. Estas ofrendas se colocan en el **altar**, la mesa del ofrecimiento. El sacerdote bendice el pan y el vino.

Además de las ofrendas del pan y el vino, ofrecemos dones monetarios. Este ofrecimiento se llama una **colecta**. El dinero ayudará a la comunidad parroquial a hacer su trabajo y cuidar de los necesitados.

El ofrecimiento monetario también es una señal de que nos ofrecemos a Dios. Estamos dispuestos a compartir tanto nuestro tiempo y nuestros talentos como nuestro tesoro con los demás.

Preguntamos

¿Por qué llamamos un sacrificio a la misa?

En la Eucaristía recordamos y celebramos el **sacrificio** de Jesús por nosotros en la cruz. Jesús ofreció su vida a su Padre para salvarnos del poder del pecado y de la muerte eterna. En cada misa se hace presente el sacrificio de Jesús. Nos ofrecemos así como ofrecemos nuestro dones. Toda la Iglesia se une con Jesús en el sacrificio de la misa.
(Catecismo, #1366–1368)

Celebramos : 43

At the **presentation of gifts**, members of the assembly bring the bread and wine to the priest. These gifts are placed on the **altar**, the table of offering. The priest blesses the bread and wine.

Along with the gifts of bread and wine, we offer gifts of money. This offering is called a **collection**. The money will help the parish community do its work and take care of those in need.

The money offering is also a sign that we offer ourselves to God. We are willing to share our time and our talents, as well as our treasure, with one another.

We Ask

Why do we call the Mass a sacrifice?

In the Eucharist we remember and celebrate Jesus' **sacrifice** for us on the cross. Jesus offered his life to his Father to save us from the power of sin and everlasting death. At every Mass Jesus' sacrifice is made present. We offer ourselves and our gifts, too. The whole Church joins with Jesus in the sacrifice of the Mass.
(Catechism, #1366–1368)

I Share My Gifts

In the space below, write about or draw two gifts you can offer to God and share with the Christian community.

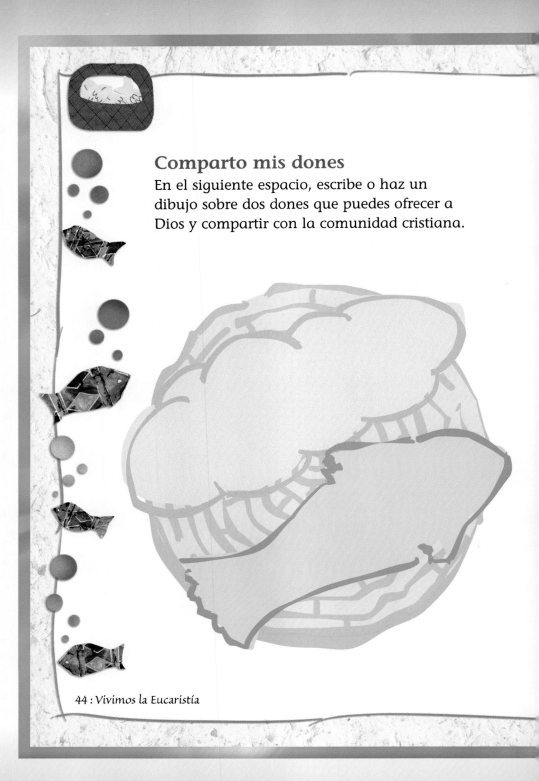

Comparto mis dones

En el siguiente espacio, escribe o haz un dibujo sobre dos dones que puedes ofrecer a Dios y compartir con la comunidad cristiana.

44 : Vivimos la Eucaristía

Por medio de tu bondad

Le pedimos a Dios que bendiga nuestros dones del pan y el vino, así como le pedimos a Dios que bendiga nuestros alimentos antes de cada comida.

Bendito seas, Señor, Dios de toda la creación.
Por tu bondad
te ofrecemos este pan
que nos ha dado la tierra
y han hecho las manos del hombre.
Se convertirá para nosotros en el
    pan de vida.
    ¡Bendito seas por siempre Dios!

Bendito seas, Señor, Dios de toda la creación.
Por tu bondad
te ofrecemos este vino
fruto de la vid y del trabajo del hombre.
Se convertirá en nuestra bebida espiritual.
    ¡Bendito seas por siempre Dios!
                    —*del Ordinario de la misa*

Through Your Goodness

We ask God to bless our gifts of bread and wine, just as we ask God to bless our food before every meal.

Blessed are you, Lord,
    God of all creation.
Through your goodness
we have this bread to offer,
which earth has given
and human hands
    have made.
It will become for us
    the bread of life.
    Blessed be God forever!

Blessed are you, Lord,
    God of all creation.
Through your goodness
we have this wine to offer,
fruit of the vine and work
    of human hands.
It will become our
    spiritual drink.
    Blessed be God forever!
                    —*from the Order of the Mass*

Chapter 6
Remembering and Giving Thanks

Dear God—Father, Son, and Holy Spirit—we remember how much you care for us. We thank you for your love that saves us. Amen!

Every year families in our country share a special holiday. We remember the good things God has done for us. We share a meal. We call this holiday Thanksgiving because we give thanks to God for our families and our country.

What things do you thank God for?

Recordar y dar gracias

Amado Dios —Padre, Hijo y Espíritu Santo— recordamos cuánto cariño nos tienes. Te damos gracias por tu amor que nos salva. ¡Amén!

Las familias en tu país comparten una fiesta especial cada año. Recordamos las cosas buenas que Dios ha hecho por nosotros. Compartimos una comida. A esta fiesta la llamamos Día de Acción de Gracias porque le damos gracias a Dios por nuestras familias y nuestro país.

¿Por qué cosas agradeces a Dios?

También le damos gracias a Dios en la misa. De hecho, la palabra **Eucaristía** significa "dar gracias". En la Eucaristía recordamos que Dios nuestro Padre envió a Jesús para salvarnos. Damos gracias y elevamos nuestros corazones a Dios en oración. Nos preparamos para compartir la comida sagrada de la Eucaristía.

We give thanks to God at Mass, too. In fact, the word **Eucharist** means "thanksgiving." In the Eucharist we remember that God our Father sent Jesus to save us. We give thanks and lift our hearts to God in prayer. We get ready to share the holy meal of the Eucharist.

Somos invitados : 47

Jesus Gives Thanks

On the night before he died, Jesus shared a special meal with his friends. They gathered to celebrate the **Passover**, a great Jewish holiday of thanksgiving.

Long ago God led the people of Israel out of the land of Egypt, where they had been slaves. He saved the people and set them free. Every year at the Passover meal, Jewish people remember God's saving love.

Jesús da gracias

En la noche antes de su muerte, Jesús compartió con sus discípulos una comida especial. Se reunieron para celebrar la **Pascua**, una fiesta importante en que los judíos dan gracias.

Hace mucho tiempo, Dios sacó al pueblo de Israel de la tierra de Egipto donde habían sido esclavos. Él salvó al pueblo y lo liberó. Cada año, en la comida de Pascua, los judíos recuerdan el amor salvador de Dios.

48 : Recordamos

En su **Última Cena** con sus discípulos, Jesús usó el pan y el vino de la comida de Pascua de una manera nueva. Tomó el pan y dijo la oración de gracias. Luego, Jesús partió el pan en pedazos y lo compartió con sus discípulos.

—Éste es mi cuerpo —dijo Jesús— que entregaré por ustedes.

Luego, Jesús tomó una copa de vino. De nuevo le dio gracias a Dios, su Padre. Pasó la copa a sus discípulos.

—Beban esto —dijo Jesús—. Ésta es la copa de mi sangre. Esta sangre se derramará para salvarlos y liberarlos.

Jesús miró con amor a sus discípulos.
—Acuérdense de mí cada vez que hagan esto —dijo Él.

—basado en el evangelio de San Mateo 26, 17–19, 26–28

At his **Last Supper** with his friends, Jesus used the bread and wine of the Passover meal in a new way. He took the bread and prayed the prayer of thanks. Then Jesus broke the bread into pieces and shared it with his friends.

"This is my body," Jesus said. "I will give it up for you."

Then Jesus took a cup of wine. Again he thanked God, his Father. He passed the cup to his friends.

"Drink this," Jesus said. "This is the cup of my blood. This blood will be poured out to save you and set you free."

Jesus looked at his friends with love. "Whenever you do this," he said, "remember me!"

—based on Matthew 26:17–19, 26–28

Recordamos : 49

Our Great Thanksgiving Prayer

At Mass we do what Jesus did at his Last Supper with his friends. And we do remember him.

The most important prayer of the Mass is called the **Eucharistic Prayer**. It is our prayer of thanksgiving to God our Father.

La oración de Acción de Gracias

En la misa hacemos lo que Jesús hizo en la Última Cena con sus discípulos y lo recordamos.

La oración más importante de la misa se llama la **Oración eucarística**. Es nuestra oración de dar gracias a Dios nuestro Padre.

50 : Celebramos

Durante la Oración eucarística, el sacerdote repite las palabras y acciones de Jesús en la Última Cena. —Éste es mi cuerpo —dice él—. Ésta es mi sangre.

Por medio de las palabras de Cristo y el poder del Espíritu Santo, el pan y el vino se convierten verdaderamente en el Cuerpo y la Sangre de Cristo. Él está con nosotros realmente en nuestra comida de acción de gracias, la Eucaristía.

¡Amén! —oramos—. ¡Sí creemos!

Preguntamos

¿Se convierten realmente el pan y el vino en el Cuerpo y la Sangre de Jesús?

Sí. Creemos que cuando se **consagran** el pan y el vino en la misa, no son más pan y vino. Jesús está verdadera y realmente presente. No comprendemos por completo cómo sucede este gran **misterio** de fe. Creemos y confiamos en que Jesús está con nosotros porque Él prometió que estaría.

(Catecismo, #1333)

During the Eucharistic Prayer the priest repeats the words and actions of Jesus at the Last Supper. "This is my body," he says. "This is the cup of my blood."

Through the words of Christ and the power of the Holy Spirit, the bread and wine truly become Jesus' Body and Blood. He is really with us in our thanksgiving meal, the Eucharist.

"Amen!" we pray. "Yes, we do believe!"

We Ask

Do the bread and wine really become Jesus' Body and Blood?

Yes. We believe that when the bread and wine are **consecrated** at Mass, they are no longer bread and wine. Jesus is truly and really present. We don't fully understand how this great **mystery** of our faith happens. We believe and trust that Jesus is with us because he promised he would be.

(Catechism, #1333)

Celebramos : 51

I Remember, I Give Thanks

Finish the prayers by writing or drawing in each box.

Dear God, I remember you love me when I . . .

Dear God, I give thanks to you for . . .

Recuerdo y doy gracias

Completa las oraciones escribiendo o dibujando en cada casilla.

Amado Dios, recuerdo que me amas cuando...

Amado Dios, te doy gracias por...

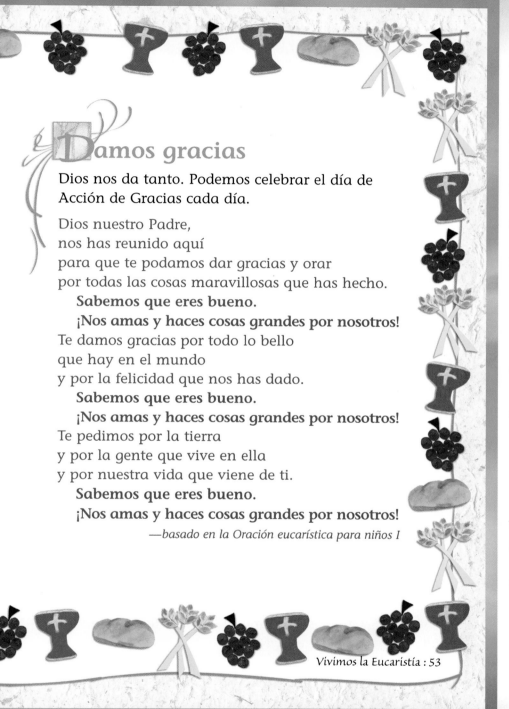

Damos gracias

Dios nos da tanto. Podemos celebrar el día de
Acción de Gracias cada día.

Dios nuestro Padre,
nos has reunido aquí
para que te podamos dar gracias y orar
por todas las cosas maravillosas que has hecho.

Sabemos que eres bueno.
¡Nos amas y haces cosas grandes por nosotros!

Te damos gracias por todo lo bello
que hay en el mundo
y por la felicidad que nos has dado.

Sabemos que eres bueno.
¡Nos amas y haces cosas grandes por nosotros!

Te pedimos por la tierra
y por la gente que vive en ella
y por nuestra vida que viene de ti.

Sabemos que eres bueno.
¡Nos amas y haces cosas grandes por nosotros!

—basado en la Oración eucarística para niños I

Vivimos la Eucaristía : 53

We Give Thanks

God gives us so much. We
can celebrate Thanksgiving
every day.

God our Father,
you have brought us here
  together
so that we can give you
  thanks and praise
for all the wonderful things
  you have done.
**We know that you
are good.**
**You love us and do
great things for us!**

We thank you for all that is
  beautiful in the world
and for the happiness you
  have given us.
**We know that you
are good.**
**You love us and do
great things for us!**

We praise you for the earth
and for the people who
  live on it
and for our life, which
  comes from you.
**We know that you
are good.**
**You love us and do
great things for us!**

—based on Eucharistic Prayer I
for Children

Chapter 7
Sharing the Bread of Life

Dear God—Father, Son, and Holy Spirit—you feed us at the table of the Eucharist. Keep us close to you forever. Amen!

Sharing a meal brings people closer together. A special party meal, sometimes called a banquet or a feast, is a time to celebrate. Family members and friends grow in love.

Have you ever shared in a banquet? Who was there? How did you feel?

Capítulo 7
Compartir el pan de vida

Amado Dios —Padre, Hijo y Espíritu Santo— Tú nos alimentas en la mesa de la Eucaristía. Mantennos cerca de ti por siempre. ¡Amén!

Compartir una comida une a la gente. Una comida especial algunas veces se conoce como banquete o fiesta, es un momento para celebrar. El amor de los familiares y amigos crece.

¿Alguna vez has compartido en un banquete? ¿Quiénes estaban allí? ¿Cómo te sentiste?

La Eucaristía es un banquete. Dios nos invita a la mesa para compartir el Cuerpo y la Sangre de Jesús en la Comunión. Antes de ir a la mesa, rezamos el **Padrenuestro**. Ésta es la oración familiar de los seguidores de Jesús. —Danos hoy nuestro pan de cada día —rezamos— y perdona nuestras ofensas.

Para mostrar que estamos dispuestos a perdonarnos y reconciliarnos entre sí, intercambiamos una **señal de paz**. Luego, el sacerdote parte la hostia grande así como Jesús partió el pan sagrado en su Última Cena. Recibimos a Jesús como el **Cordero de Dios**, que aleja nuestros pecados y nos trae paz.

The Eucharist is our banquet. God invites us to the table to share Jesus' own Body and Blood in Communion. Before we come to the table, we pray the **Lord's Prayer**. This is the family prayer of the followers of Jesus. "Give us this day our daily bread," we pray, "and forgive us our trespasses."

To show that we are willing to forgive one another and make up, we exchange a **sign of peace**. Then the priest breaks the large Host as Jesus broke the sacred Bread at his Last Supper. We welcome Jesus as the **Lamb of God**, who takes away our sins and brings us peace.

Somos invitados : 55

The Bread That Gives Life

After Jesus had fed the crowd with only five loaves of bread and a few fish, people wanted him to perform more **miracles**. "You are like Moses," the people said. "When the people of Israel were hungry in the desert, Moses gave them **manna**, bread from heaven."

"You are not remembering the whole story," Jesus told them. "It was not Moses who gave food to the people. It was God, our Father in heaven. God gives people the real bread from heaven."

"Lord, give us this bread always!" the people begged.

El pan que da vida

Después de que Jesús había alimentado a la multitud con sólo cinco panes y unos cuantos pescados, la gente quería que efectuara más **milagros**. —Eres como Moisés —decía la gente—. Cuando el pueblo de Israel estaba hambriento en el desierto, Moisés les dio el **maná**, el pan del cielo.

—No recuerdan toda la historia —les dijo Jesús—. No fue Moisés el que alimentó al pueblo. Fue Dios, nuestro Padre en el cielo. Dios les da a las personas el pan verdadero del cielo.

¡Dios, danos siempre este pan! —rogaba el pueblo.

—Yo soy el pan que da vida —contestó Jesús—. Mi Padre me envió para traerles vida eterna. Nadie que viene a mí estará hambriento. Nadie que cree en mí estará sediento.

Jesús continuó. —Soy el pan del cielo. A la postre, la gente que comió maná en el desierto, murió al igual que todos los seres humanos. Pero si comparten mi carne y sangre, vivirán eternamente con Dios.

—¿De qué habla? —preguntaron algunos. Pero otros recordaron cómo se sintieron cuando Jesús los alimentó con pan y pescado. Creyeron lo que decía.

—*basado en el evangelio de San Juan 6, 30–58*

Recordamos : 57

"I myself am the bread that gives life," Jesus answered. "My Father sent me to bring you life that lasts forever. No one who comes to me will ever be hungry. No one who believes in me will ever be thirsty."

Jesus continued. "I am the bread from heaven. The people who ate manna in the desert eventually died, as all humans die. But if you share my own flesh and blood, you will live forever with God."

"What is he talking about?" some people asked. But others remembered how they felt when Jesus fed them with bread and fish. They believed what he said.

—*based on John 6:30–58*

Holy Communion

When the time comes for Communion, the priest invites us to the table. "This is the Lamb of God, who takes away the sin of the world," he says, holding up the large Host. "Happy are we who are called to his supper!"

To receive Communion, we come forward in a procession. We wait our turn respectfully. We hold our hands up, cupping them with one hand on top of the other. The priest or **Eucharistic minister** places the Host in our hands and says, "The Body of Christ." We answer, "Amen!"

Then we step aside and eat the sacred Bread.

La sagrada Comunión

Cuando llega el momento de la Comunión, el sacerdote nos invita a la mesa. —Éste es el Cordero de Dios, que quita el pecado del mundo —dice él, sosteniendo la hostia grande—. ¡Dichosos los invitados a su cena!

Para recibir la Comunión, nos acercamos en una procesión. Esperamos nuestro turno con respeto. Mantenemos nuestras manos levantadas, una encima de la otra. El sacerdote o el **ministro de la Eucaristía** coloca la hostia en nuestras manos y dice: —El Cuerpo de Cristo. Nosotros contestamos: —¡Amén!

Luego, nos alejamos y comemos el pan sagrado.

58 : Celebramos

Algunos domingos podemos recibir la Comunión del cáliz. Después de tomar la hostia, vamos al diácono o ministro de la Eucaristía que sostiene el cáliz con vino consagrado. El ministro dice: —La Sangre de Cristo. Nosotros contestamos: —¡Amén! Cuando nos ofrecen el cáliz, tomamos un sorbo.

Jesús está realmente presente en las dos formas de la Eucaristía.

Después de recibir la Comunión, regresamos a nuestros lugares. Quizás se cante una canción de comunión o haya un momento de silencio.

Preguntamos

¿Quién puede recibir la Comunión?

Los católicos bautizados que han celebrado la Primera Comunión pueden comulgar en la misa. La persona que haya cometido pecado mortal, debe ser **absuelto** en el **sacramento de la Reconciliación** antes de recibir la Comunión.
(Catecismo, #1384–1389)

On many Sundays we may also receive Communion from the cup. After swallowing the Host, we go to the deacon or Eucharistic minister who is holding the cup of consecrated Wine. The minister says, "The Blood of Christ." We answer, "Amen!" When we are offered the cup, we take a small sip.

Jesus is truly present in both forms of the Eucharist.

After receiving Communion, we return to our places. There may be a Communion song or a time of silent prayer.

We Ask

Who can receive Communion?

Baptized Catholics who have celebrated First Communion may receive Communion at Mass. A person who has committed mortal sin must receive **absolution** in the **Sacrament of Reconciliation** before receiving Communion.
(Catechism, #1384–1389)

Celebramos : 59

My First Communion

In the frame, draw or glue a picture of your First Communion. On the line, write the date of your First Communion.

Mi Primera Comunión

En el marco, dibuja o pega una ilustración de tu Primera Comunión. Sobre la línea, escribe la fecha de tu Primera Comunión.

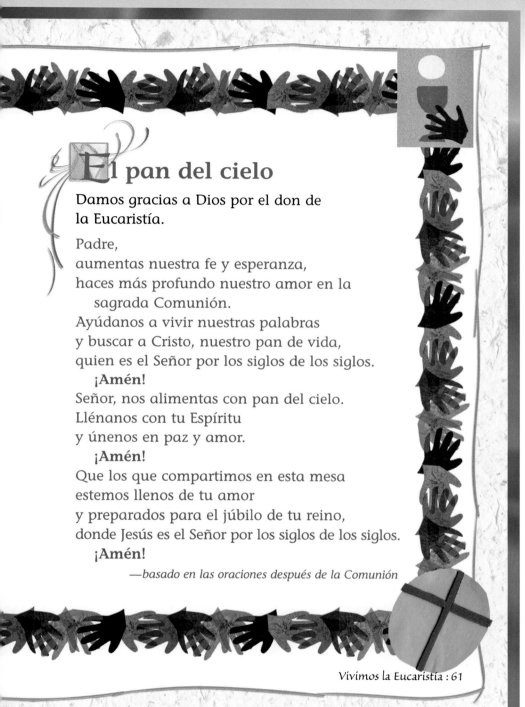

El pan del cielo

Damos gracias a Dios por el don de la Eucaristía.

Padre,
aumentas nuestra fe y esperanza,
haces más profundo nuestro amor en la
    sagrada Comunión.
Ayúdanos a vivir nuestras palabras
y buscar a Cristo, nuestro pan de vida,
quien es el Señor por los siglos de los siglos.
    ¡Amén!
Señor, nos alimentas con pan del cielo.
Llénanos con tu Espíritu
y únenos en paz y amor.
    ¡Amén!
Que los que compartimos en esta mesa
estemos llenos de tu amor
y preparados para el júbilo de tu reino,
donde Jesús es el Señor por los siglos de los siglos.
    ¡Amén!

—*basado en las oraciones después de la Comunión*

Vivimos la Eucaristía : 61

Bread from Heaven

We thank God for the gift of the Eucharist.

Father,
you increase our faith
    and hope,
you deepen our love in
    Holy Communion.
Help us live by your words
and seek Christ, our Bread
    of Life,
who is Lord for ever
    and ever.
    Amen!
Lord, you feed us with
    bread from heaven.
Fill us with your Spirit,
and make us one in peace
    and love.
    Amen!
May we who share at
    this table
be filled with your love
and prepared for the joy
    of your kingdom,
where Jesus is Lord for ever
    and ever.
    Amen!

—*based on Prayers after Communion*

Chapter 8
Going Forth to Love and Serve

Dear God—Father, Son, and Holy Spirit—thank you for coming to us in the Eucharist. Send us out into the world to share your love. Amen!

Have you ever been sent to tell someone something or to do a special job?

Being sent means that you are trusted. You are responsible. Someone is counting on you. Without you the message will not be shared. The job will not get done.

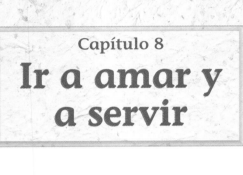

Capítulo 8
Ir a amar y a servir

Amado Dios —Padre, Hijo y Espíritu Santo— gracias por llegar a nosotros en la Eucaristía. Envíanos al mundo para compartir tu amor. ¡Amén!

¿Alguna vez te han enviado a decirle algo a alguien o a hacer un trabajo especial?

Cuando te envían es porque tienen confianza en ti. Eres responsable. Alguien depende de ti. Sin ti, el mensaje no se dará. El trabajo no se hará.

No one is too young or too old to be trusted with this mission. The Eucharist gives us what we need to bring good news to others. Receiving Jesus in Holy Communion strengthens us to love and serve. We go out with God's blessing.

Al final de la misa, a cada uno de nosotros se nos envía a llevar el mensaje del amor de Dios. Se nos envía a cumplir el trabajo de Jesús en el mundo. Incluso la palabra **misa** proviene de una palabra que significa "ser enviado a una **misión**".

Nadie es muy joven o muy viejo para que se le confíe una misión. La Eucaristía nos da lo que necesitamos para llevar las buenas noticias a otros. Al recibir a Jesucristo en la sagrada Comunión, nos reforzamos para amar y servir. Partimos con la bendición de Dios.

In the Breaking of the Bread

It was the third day after Jesus died on the cross. Cleopas and I were walking home from Jerusalem to our town, Emmaus. We were sad. Then another traveler joined us. We did not know who he was. He asked us why we were so sad.

Cleopas and I told the traveler all about Jesus. We talked about what a great teacher he was and how he fed us with Bread from heaven. We thought he was the **Messiah** sent by God to save us. But now he was dead.

The traveler shook his head. "Foolish people!" he said. "Don't you know that the Scriptures say the Messiah will give up his life for you?" And he explained God's word to us as we walked along.

We reached home as the sun was setting. "Stay and eat with us," Cleopas invited the traveler. "It's nearly night."

Al partir el pan

Era el tercer día después de la muerte de Jesús en la cruz. Cleofás y yo caminábamos a la casa desde Jerusalén a nuestro pueblo de Emaús. Estábamos tristes.

Entonces, otro viajero se unió. No sabíamos quién era. Nos preguntó por qué estábamos tan tristes.

Cleofás y yo le contamos al viajero todo acerca de Jesús. Le contamos que era un gran maestro y cómo nos alimentó con el pan del cielo. Creíamos que era el **Mesías** enviado por Dios para nuestra salvación. Pero ahora estaba muerto.

El viajero negó con su cabeza y dijo: —¡Pueblo absurdo! ¿No saben que las Escrituras dicen que el Mesías daría la vida por ustedes?— Y nos explicó la palabra de Dios mientras caminábamos.

Llegamos a casa cuando se ocultaba el sol. —Quédate y come con nosotros —dijo Cleofás invitando al viajero—. Es casi de noche.

Al sentarnos en la mesa, el viajero tomó el pan, lo bendijo y lo partió. Y al darnos el pan, comprendimos. ¡El viajero era Jesús! ¡Dios, el Padre, lo había resucitado de la muerte!

En un momento, Jesús había desaparecido. Nos devolvimos a Jerusalén. Entramos en el salón donde la madre de Jesús y sus amigos estaban reunidos.

—¡Jesús está vivo! —dijo Pedro al recibirnos con júbilo.

—¡Lo sabemos! —dije—. Caminó con nosotros. Nos explicó la palabra de Dios. Y lo reconocimos al partir el pan.

—basado en el evangelio de San Lucas 24, 13–35

As we sat at the table, the traveler took the bread. He blessed it and broke it. And as he gave it to us, we suddenly understood. The traveler was Jesus! God the Father had raised him from death!

In the blink of an eye, Jesus was gone. We ran all the way back to Jerusalem. We burst into the room where Jesus' mother and his friends had gathered.

"Jesus is alive!" Peter said as he greeted us joyfully.

"We know!" I said. "He walked with us on the road. He shared God's word with us. And we recognized him in the breaking of the Bread."

—based on Luke 24:13–35

We Are Sent

Like Cleopas and his friend, we meet Jesus in the breaking of the sacred Bread. In the Eucharist Jesus walks with us. He shares God's word with us. Jesus offers his life to the Father in the power of the Holy Spirit. He comes to us in Communion.

And like those friends of Jesus, we want to share the joyful good news that Jesus is alive. At the end of the Mass, we are sent out to serve others. "Go in peace to love and serve the Lord," the priest or deacon says. "Thanks be to God!" we answer.

Somos enviados

Al igual que Cleofás y su amigo, nosotros encontramos a Jesús al partir el pan sagrado. En la Eucaristía, Jesús camina con nosotros. Nos explica la palabra de Dios. Jesús ofrece su vida al Padre con el poder del Espíritu Santo. Se nos acerca en la Comunión.

Y al igual que los amigos de Jesús, queremos compartir el júbilo de que Jesús está vivo. Al final de la misa, se nos envía a servir a los demás. —Vayan en paz a amar y servir al Señor —repite el sacerdote o diácono—. ¡Demos gracias a Dios! —respondemos.

66 : Celebramos

Cuando salimos de la iglesia después de misa, somos diferentes. La Eucaristía nos cambia. Nos lleva más cerca de Dios y del prójimo. La Eucaristía nos limpia los pecados menos graves. Nos ayuda a estar en paz con los demás.

En la Eucaristía nos convertimos en un cuerpo, al igual que muchos granos de trigo forman un pan. Así que al salir, reconocemos a Jesús en nuestro prójimo. Amamos y servimos a Jesús cuando amamos y servimos a los demás.

Preguntamos

¿Cómo representa la Eucaristía el reino de Dios?

Jesús vino a anunciar el reino de Dios de justicia, amor y paz. Ese reino está tanto entre nosotros como por venir en plenitud. En la Eucaristía probamos un poco lo que será el banquete celestial que compartiremos con todos los fieles en la plenitud del reino de Dios. Fortalecidos por la Eucaristía, trabajamos para llevar justicia, amor y paz a todos. *(Catecismo, #1402–1405)*

Celebramos : 67

When we leave the church after Mass, we are different from when we came in. The Eucharist changes us. It brings us closer to God and to one another. The Eucharist takes away our less serious sins. It helps us make peace with everyone.

In the Eucharist we become one body, just as many grains of wheat make one loaf of bread. So when we go out into the world, we recognize Jesus in everyone. We love and serve Jesus when we love and serve one another.

We Ask

How is the Eucharist a sign of God's kingdom?

Jesus came to announce God's kingdom of justice, love, and peace. That kingdom is both here in our midst and yet to come in fullness. In the Eucharist we receive a taste of the heavenly banquet we will share with all faithful people in the fullness of God's kingdom. Strengthened by the Eucharist, we work to bring justice, love, and peace to everyone. *(Catechism, #1402–1405)*

I Love and Serve

Draw or write three things you will do to share God's love with others.

Amo y sirvo

Dibuja o escribe tres cosas que harás para compartir el amor de Dios con los demás.

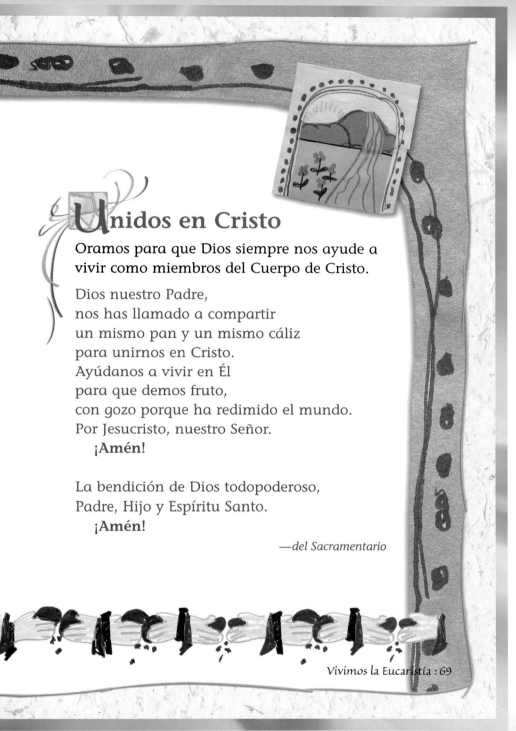

Unidos en Cristo

Oramos para que Dios siempre nos ayude a vivir como miembros del Cuerpo de Cristo.

Dios nuestro Padre,
nos has llamado a compartir
un mismo pan y un mismo cáliz
para unirnos en Cristo.
Ayúdanos a vivir en Él
para que demos fruto,
con gozo porque ha redimido el mundo.
Por Jesucristo, nuestro Señor.
   ¡Amén!

La bendición de Dios todopoderoso,
Padre, Hijo y Espíritu Santo.
   ¡Amén!

—*del Sacramentario*

Vivimos la Eucaristía : 69

One in Christ

We pray that God will help us live always as members of the Body of Christ.

God our Father,
you have called us to share
the one bread and one cup
and so become one in
   Christ.
Help us live in him
that we may bear fruit,
rejoicing that he has
   redeemed the world.
We ask this through Christ
   our Lord.
   Amen!

May almighty God bless us,
the Father, the Son, and
   the Holy Spirit.
   Amen!

—*from the Sacramentary*

Oraciones católicas

La Señal de la Cruz

En el nombre del Padre,
del Hijo
y del Espíritu Santo.
Amén.

El Padrenuestro

Padre nuestro, que estás en el cielo,
santificado sea tu nombre;
venga a nosotros tu reino;
hágase tu voluntad en la tierra como en el cielo.
Danos hoy nuestro pan de cada día
y perdona nuestras ofensas
como nosotros perdonamos a los que nos ofenden.
No nos dejes caer en tentación
y líbranos del mal.
Amén.

El Avemaría

Dios te salve, María, llena eres de gracia;
el Señor está contigo.
Bendita tú eres entre todas las mujeres
y bendito es el fruto de tu vientre, Jesús.
Santa María, Madre de Dios,
ruega por nosotros, pecadores,
ahora y en la hora de nuestra muerte.
Amén.

El Gloria (Doxología)

Gloria al Padre,
y al Hijo,
y al Espíritu Santo,
como era en un principio,
ahora y siempre,
por los siglos de los siglos.
Amén.

Bendición antes de la Primera Comunión

Que el Señor Jesús toque tus oídos para recibir su palabra
y tu boca para proclamar su fe.
Que vayas con gozo a su cena
para alabar y glorificar a Dios.
Amén.

Oración antes de la Comunión

Qué sagrada es esta cena
en la que Cristo es nuestro alimento;
su pasión es recordada,
la gracia llena nuestros corazones
y recibimos la promesa de la gloria futura.

—basada en una oración de Tomás de Aquino

Acción de gracias después de la Comunión

Señor nuestro Dios,
honramos la memoria de San Pío X
y todos tus santos
al compartir el pan del cielo.
Que fortalezca nuestra fe
y nos unifique en tu amor.
Te lo pedimos en nombre de Jesucristo nuestro Señor.
Amén.

La vida de Jesús

Éstos son algunos sucesos importantes en la vida de Jesús como se describen en los Evangelios.

La anunciación

Dios envió al ángel Gabriel para decirle a María que iba a ser la madre de Jesús, el Hijo de Dios.

La natividad

Jesús nació en Belén en un refugio para animales. Los ángeles anunciaron a los pastores las buenas noticias del nacimiento del Salvador.

La presentación

En el templo en Jerusalén, María y José presentaron la ofrenda de gracias por el nacimiento de Jesús. Simeón y Ana, dos profetas, reconocieron a Jesús como el Mesías.

La epifanía

Maestros sabios de tierras lejanas fueron a adorar a Jesús.

El escape a Egipto

Un rey furioso amenazó con matar a Jesús. A José, su padre adoptivo, se le advirtió en un sueño que llevara a María y a Jesús a Egipto.

El joven Jesús en el templo

En un viaje a Jerusalén por la fiesta de Pascua, Jesús se separó de María y José. Lo buscaron y lo hallaron en el templo, hablando de la palabra de Dios con los sabios maestros.

El bautismo de Jesús por Juan

Cuando Jesús tenía unos 30 años de edad, comenzó sus enseñanzas entre el pueblo. Fue bautizado en el río Jordán por su primo Juan, un profeta.

La tentación en el desierto

Después de su bautismo, Jesús fue solo al desierto para rezar y ayunar. Fue tentado por Satanás, pero obedeció a Dios, su Padre.

Jesús llama a los apóstoles

Jesús reunió a un grupo de amigos especiales y ayudantes llamados apóstoles. Otros hombres y mujeres también lo siguieron y ayudaron en su trabajo.

Jesús enseña

Jesús enseñó el amor de Dios a multitudes de personas. Contó historias llamadas parábolas.

Jesús cura

En el nombre de Dios, su Padre, Jesús curó a personas enfermas o preocupadas. Perdonó los pecados.

Jesús muestra el amor de Dios

Jesús hizo milagros, o sea, señales poderosas del amor de Dios. Convirtió el agua en vino en un matrimonio. Alimentó a miles de personas con poca comida. Revivió a muertos.

Jesús entra en Jerusalén

Después de tres años de enseñar, Jesús entró en Jerusalén para la Pascua. Sabía que enfrentaría la muerte porque ciertos líderes estaban enojados con Él. Algunas personas, que hacían señas con las palmas, dieron la bienvenida a Jesús como el rey al entrar en la ciudad.

La Última Cena

En la noche antes de morir, Jesús celebró la cena de Pascua con sus amigos. Les lavó sus pies como señal de que debían servir a los demás. Se compartió a sí mismo con ellos en la primera Eucaristía.

En el huerto

Después de la cena, Jesús fue al huerto con sus amigos a rezar. Uno de ellos lo traicionó entregándolo a los líderes que querían matarlo. A Jesús lo arrestaron y lo llevaron a la cárcel.

El juicio

Jesús fue acusado de actuar contra la ley. Fue castigado con látigos y golpeado. Los líderes sentenciaron a muerte a Jesús.

La crucifixión

A Jesús lo ejecutaron clavándolo en la cruz. Mientras colgaba en la cruz,  perdonó a aquéllos que lo habían sentenciado. Luego murió.

El sepulcro

El cuerpo de Jesús fue llevado a una tumba. Ésta estaba sellada con grandes piedras.

La resurrección

En el tercer día después de la muerte de Jesús, Dios el Padre lo volvió a la vida. Cuando los amigos de Jesús visitaron su tumba, se dieron cuenta que se había movido la piedra y que la tumba estaba vacía. Más tarde, Jesús se les apareció en gloria.

La ascensión

Cuarenta días después de resucitar, Jesús regresó a su Padre en los cielos. Jesús prometió enviar al Espíritu Santo para que enseñara y guiara a la Iglesia.

La sagrada Comunión

Recibir la sagrada Comunión

Los católicos siguen estas reglas y prácticas para mostrar respeto por la Eucaristía:

- Sólo los católicos bautizados pueden recibir la Comunión.

- Para recibir la sagrada Comunión, debemos estar libres de pecado mortal. Debemos arrepentirnos de cualquier pecado venial cometido desde la última Reconciliación. Cuando nos arrepentimos, la sagrada Comunión nos libra del pecado venial.

- Para honrar al Señor, ayunamos por una hora antes de recibir la Comunión. No comemos ni bebemos, excepto agua o medicina.

- A los católicos se nos requiere recibir la sagrada Comunión por lo menos una vez al año, si es posible durante Semana Santa. Pero se nos anima a recibir la Comunión cada vez que vamos a misa.

- A los católicos se nos permite recibir la Comunión en una segunda misa en el mismo día.

Cómo recibir la Comunión

Cuando recibimos a Jesús en la sagrada Comunión, lo hacemos con todo nuestro cuerpo, mente y espíritu.

Éstos son los pasos a seguir cuando recibimos la Comunión:

- Enlaza las manos y canta el himno de la Comunión mientras caminas hacia el altar.

- Cuando sea tu turno, puedes recibir la hostia consagrada en tu mano o en tu lengua. Para recibirla en tus manos, pon las palmas hacia arriba, una mano debajo de la otra y colócalas en forma de taza. Para recibir la hostia en tu lengua, enlaza las manos y abre tu boca sacando la lengua.

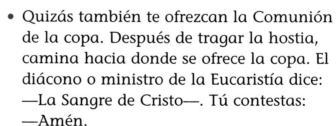

- El sacerdote o ministro de la Eucaristía dice: —El cuerpo de Cristo—. Y tú contestas: —Amén. El sacerdote o ministro coloca la hostia en tu mano o en tu lengua.

- Retírate y detente. Si has recibido la hostia en tu mano, cuidadosamente tómala en tu palma y colócala en tu boca. Mastica y traga la hostia.

- Quizás también te ofrezcan la Comunión de la copa. Después de tragar la hostia, camina hacia donde se ofrece la copa. El diácono o ministro de la Eucaristía dice: —La Sangre de Cristo—. Tú contestas: —Amén.

- Toma la copa del sacerdote, diácono o ministro. Toma un sorbo y cuidadosamente regrésala.

- Calladamente regresa a tu lugar. Reza una oración de gracias.

Glosario ilustrado de la misa

altar
La mesa de la Eucaristía. En el altar se ofrece el sacrificio de la misa a Dios.

ambón
Atril o pedestal de lectura desde donde se proclaman las Escrituras. Algunas veces el ambón se conoce como "la mesa de la palabra".

angarillas
Jarras o recipientes pequeños para el agua y el vino que se usan en la misa. Muchas parroquias usan jarras grandes para sostener el vino especialmente si las personas recibirán la Comunión del cáliz.

cáliz
La copa especial que se usa en la misa para el vino que se convierte en la Sangre de Cristo.

congregación
La comunidad se reúne para celebrar la Eucaristía u otra liturgia sacramental.

diácono

Un hombre ordenado para servir a la Iglesia, bautizando, proclamando el Evangelio, predicando, ayudando al sacerdote en la misa, atestiguando en matrimonios haciendo obras de caridad.

Eucaristía

El sacramento de la presencia de Jesús bajo la forma del pan y vino sagrados. Recibimos el Cuerpo y la Sangre de Jesús como la sagrada Comunión durante la celebración de la Eucaristía, es decir, la misa. La palabra *Eucaristía* significa "dar gracias".

Evangelios

Un libro decorado que contiene las lecturas de los cuatro Evangelios que se usan durante la Liturgia de la Palabra.

hostia

Un pedazo redondo de pan sin levadura que se usa en la misa. Cuando se consagra la hostia, se convierte en el Cuerpo y la Sangre de Cristo. Recibimos la hostia consagrada en la sagrada Comunión.

incienso

Aceites y especias que se queman para producir un humo con olor dulce. En la misa y en otras celebraciones litúrgicas, a veces se usa el incienso para demostrar honor ante las cosas sagradas y como una señal de la elevación de nuestras oraciones a Dios.

Leccionario
El libro de las lecturas de las Escrituras que se usa en la misa.

lector
Un ministro que proclama la palabra de Dios en la misa o en otras celebraciones litúrgicas.

monaguillo
Un ministro, por lo general una persona joven, que ayuda al sacerdote y al diácono en la misa. Una persona de más edad que desempeña este papel se conoce como un **acólito**.

ofrenda
Los regalos que damos en la misa. Los miembros de la congregación llevan la ofrenda de pan y vino al altar. También se ofrece dinero, llamado la *colecta*, para asistir con el trabajo de la Iglesia.

patena
El plato que se usa en la misa para poner el pan que se convertirá en el Cuerpo y la Sangre de Cristo.

pila bautismal

El recipiente o pileta de agua que se usa para el Bautismo.
La palabra *pila* significa "fuente".

sacerdote

Un hombre que es ordenado para servir a Dios y a la
Iglesia al celebrar los sacramentos, predicar y presidir
la misa.

Sacramentario

El libro de oraciones que usa el sacerdote en la misa.
También se le llama **misal**. Los miembros de la
congregación pueden usar folletos también llamados
misales para seguir las lecturas, respuestas y oraciones.

sagrario

Un recipiente para hostias. Un sagrario puede tener el
menor número de hostias consagradas que se usa para la
Comunión. Un sagrario cubierto también tiene el Sagrado
Sacramento en el santuario.

santuario

La parte de la iglesia donde se encuentran el altar y el
ambón. La palabra *santuario* significa "sitio sagrado".

solista

El ministro que dirige el canto en la misa y durante otras celebraciones eclesiásticas.

tabernáculo

La caja, cofre o envase donde se guarda el Santísimo Sacramento. El tabernáculo puede encontrarse en el santuario o en una capilla eucarística o área especial. Una lámpara o una vela se mantiene encendida cerca del tabernáculo como señal de la presencia de Jesús. La palabra *tabernáculo* significa "sitio de reunión".

ujier

Un ministro de hospitalidad que da la bienvenida a los miembros de la congregación que asisten a la misa y ayuda a dirigir las procesiones y colectas.

vestiduras

La ropa especial que lleva el sacerdote y otros ministros en la misa y otras celebraciones litúrgicas. El sacerdote lleva un **alba**, una **casulla** y una **estola**. El diácono lleva una **dalmática** o un alba y una estola. Los colores de las vestiduras por lo general indican la temporada del año litúrgico.

vino

Una bebida hecha de jugo de uva que se ha fermentado. En la misa, el vino consagrado se convierte en el Cuerpo y la Sangre de Cristo. Podemos recibir el vino consagrado de la copa durante la Comunión.